ORGANIC SYNTHESES

ORGANIC SYNTHESES

AN ANNUAL PUBLICATION OF SATISFACTORY METHODS FOR THE PREPARATION OF ORGANIC CHEMICALS

VOLUME 56

1977

JOHN WILEY AND SONS
NEW YORK · LONDON · SYDNEY · TORONTO

Library of Congress Catalog Card Number: 21-17747
ISBN 0-471-02218-7

Printed in the United States of America

10 9 8 7 6 5 4 3 2 1

NOMENCLATURE

Common names of the compounds are used throughout this volume. Preparations appear in the alphabetical order of common names of the compound or names of the synthetic procedures. The *Chemical Abstracts* indexing name for each title compound, if it differs from the common name, is given as a subtitle. Because of the major shift to new systematic nomenclature adopted by *Chemical Abstracts* in 1972, many common names used in the text are immediately followed by the bracketed, new names. Whenever two names are concurrently in use, the correct *Chemical Abstracts* name is adopted. The prefix n- is deleted from n-alkanes and n-alkyls. In the case of amines, both the common and systematic names are used, depending on which one the Editor-in-Chief feels is more appropriate. All reported dimensions are now expressed in Système International units.

Submission of Preparations

Chemists are invited to submit for publication in *Organic Syntheses* procedures for the preparation of compounds that are of general interest, as well as procedures that illustrate synthetic methods of general utility. It is fundamental to the usefulness of *Organic Syntheses* that submitted procedures represent optimum conditions, and the procedures should have been checked carefully by the submitters, not only for yield and physical properties of the products, but also for any hazards that may be involved. Full details of all manipulations should be described, and the range of yield should be reported rather than the maximum yield obtainable by an operator who has had considerable experience with the preparation. For each solid product the melting-point range should be reported, and for each liquid product the range of boiling point and refractive index should be included. In most instances it is desirable to include additional physical properties of the product, such as ultraviolet, infrared, mass, or nuclear magnetic resonance spectra, and criteria of purity such as gas chromatographic data. In the event that any of the reactants are not commercially available at reasonable cost, their preparation should be described in as complete detail and in the same manner as the preparation of the product of major interest. The sources of the reactants should be described in notes, and physical properties such as boiling point, index of refraction, and melting point of the reactants should be included except where standard commercial grades are specified.

Beginning with Volume 49, Methods of Preparation (Sec. 3) and Merits of the Preparation (Sec. 4) have been combined into Discussion (Sec. 3). In this section should be described other practical methods for accomplishing the purpose of the procedure that have appeared in the literature. It is unnecessary to mention methods that have been published but are of no practical synthetic value. Those features of the procedure that recommend it for publication in *Organic Syntheses* should be cited (synthetic method of considerable scope, specific compound of interest not likely to be made available commercially, method that gives better yield or is less laborious than other methods, etc.). If possible, a brief discussion of the scope and limitations of the procedure as applied to other examples, as well as a comparison of the particular method with the other methods cited, should be included. If necessary to the understanding or use of the method for related syntheses, a brief discussion of the mechanism may be placed in this section. The present emphasis of *Organic Syntheses* is on model procedures rather than on specific compounds (although the latter are still welcomed), and the Discussion should be written to help the reader decide whether and how to use the procedure in his own research. Three copies of each procedure should be submitted to the Secretary of the Editorial Board. It is sometimes helpful to the Board if there is an accompanying letter setting forth the features of the preparations that are of interest.

Additions, corrections, and improvements to the preparations previously published are welcomed and should be directed to the Secretary.

WILLIAM WEAVER HARTMAN

February 2, 1897–October 16, 1975

Born in Chicago, William Weaver Hartman was educated at Northwestern University and the University of Chicago, completing his courses in 1918. From June to December 1918 he worked at the Bureau of Mines in the Chemical Warfare Service, World War I, Washington, D.C., and as a chemist for Morris and Co., Union Stock Yards, Chicago, from July to October 1919.

In 1918 Dr. C. E. K. Mees, Eastman Kodak's first director of research, wrote a letter to George Eastman about a critical situation facing American chemistry. War had shut off Germany as a supplier of synthetic organic reagents, and the only American source was a small laboratory at the University of Illinois. Dr. Mees said, "The continuance of effective research in pure organic chemistry is largely dependent upon the establishment of a satisfactory source of synthetic organic reagents. No such source is at present in sight. . . . Unless something is done immediately, organic research will languish. . . ." He proposed establishing a nonprofit department of synthetic chemistry as part of the Eastman Kodak Research Laboratory. Mr. Eastman simply wrote "Approved." This was the one word that launched Kodak into the chemistry business.

The new synthetic chemistry department was placed under Hans T. Clarke, who had a very small staff of a few assistants. The first man he hired as an organic chemist, on October 22, 1919, was W. W. Hartman, who was just out of the army. On July 10, 1929, he became an assistant superintendent, then superintendent on September 1, 1947. He retired on January 1, 1959. The current title of the department is the Synthetic Chemistry Division of the Research Laboratory.

He was elected to *Organic Syntheses* in 1931 and was Editor-in-Chief of Vol. 14 in 1934. During his 10 years of active participation on the Board he submitted 23 preparations and checked 38. Hartman was one of the original incorporators of Organic Syntheses Inc., on October 9, 1939 and served as Treasurer for 17 years until April 1, 1957.

He had considerable financial skill and was well informed on the stock market. When the surplus from the sales of *Organic Syntheses* became more than was anticipated for a nonprofit organization, he was on the committee that arranged for its investment.

He never tired of playing bridge. An inveterate practical joker, he always did things in a big way. Among his hobbies was woodworking— he had a shop filled with all kinds of power tools. He had a very successful farm, where he raised both Guernsey cattle and cherries. As a spectator he enjoyed sports, such as major league baseball; when he attended American Chemical Society national meetings he attended any available game. In later years he followed horse racing. He bought a condominium at Daytona Beach, Florida, where he and his wife stayed for 6 months of the winter, returning to Rochester for the summer season. It was there that he died.

Charles F. H. Allen

WILLIAM E. PARHAM

September, 9, 1922–May 21, 1976

William Eugene Parham, Treasurer and member of the Board of Directors and of the Advisory Board of Organic Syntheses, died May 21, 1976 of a coronary occlusion near his summer home on Deer Lake, near Deer River, Minnesota, at the age of 53. Dr. Parham joined the Board of Editors on September 7, 1958 and served as Editor-in-Chief of Volume 44 of *Organic Syntheses* in 1964. He became a member of the Advisory Board and was elected to the Board of Directors in 1966, and served as Vice President from 1969 to 1974, at which time he succeeded Richard S. Schreiber as Treasurer. As Treasurer, Dr. Parham was very effective in securing competent legal counsel for *Organic Syntheses* and in clarifying its foundation tax status with the Internal Revenue Service.

Born in Denison, Texas on September 9, 1922, he was the son of Charles Eugene Parham and Jewel Looney Parham. He attended Highland Park High School in Dallas, Texas from 1935 to 1939, and then Southern Methodist University, where he received his B.S. degree in 1943. He was later (in 1959) elected to Phi Beta Kappa after a local chapter was established there. At the University of Illinois in Urbana he obtained his M.S. and Ph.D. degrees in 1944 and 1946. He carried out his Ph.D. research with Professor Reynold C. Fuson (Editor-in-Chief of Volume 18 of *Organic Syntheses*). While at Illinois he married Wilma Louise (Billie Lou) Johnston on March 9, 1946. In 1946 he went directly to the University of Minnesota as an assistant professor, becoming an associate professor in 1950 and a full professor in 1955. In 1958 he succeeded Professor Lee Irvin Smith (Editor-in-Chief of Volumes 22 and 23 of *Organic Syntheses*) as Chief of the Division of Organic Chemistry at Minnesota, continuing to serve in a comparable capacity until 1971. In 1972 he became the R. J. Reynolds Professor of Chemistry at Duke University and continued in that position until his death.

Dr. Parham served as a chemical consultant to E. I. du Pont de Nemours and Company beginning in 1953, to the Sinclair Oil Corporation from 1952 to 1969 and to its successor company, the Atlantic Richfield Company, since 1969, and to the Surgeon General, on anti-radiation drugs, from 1959 to 1961. He served on advisory boards for research grants, including those of the National Science Foundation, the Army Office of Ordnance Research, the National Institutes of Health, the Office of the Surgeon General, and, at the time of his death, the Petroleum Research Fund. His national activities in the American Chemical Society included being Secretary-Treasurer and member of the Executive Committee of the Organic Division (1954–1959) and its Chairman-Elect (1960) and Chairman (1961), member (1954–1957) and Chairman (1956–1957) of the Committee of the Divisional Officers Group, membership on the Council (1954–1957), Committee on National Meetings and Divisional Activities (1954–1957), Committee of Visiting Associates of the Committee on Professional Training (from 1957 on), and the Canvassing Committee for the A.C.S. Award for Creative Work in Synthetic Organic Chemistry (1959). In addition to *Organic Syntheses*, he served on the editorial advisory boards of the *Journal of Organic Chemistry* (1954–1959), Chemical Reviews (1959–1968), and the *Advances in Chemistry* series of the American Chemical Society (1969–1972). He served as the Associate Editor of Volume 13 of *Organic Reactions*, published in 1963, and was the author of the advanced textbook, *Syntheses and Reactions in Organic Chemistry*, published in 1970. His awards included a Guggenheim Fellowship for study at the California Institute of Technology and the University of Groningen in the Netherlands in 1961–1962, an Honorary Doctor of Science from Southern Methodist University in 1966, the Kresge-Hooker Lectureship at Wayne State University (1968), a Robert A. Welch Foundation Lectureship (Texas, 1969), and the Minnesota Award of the Minnesota Section of the American Chemical Society (1970). In 1966 he served as chairman of the board of trustees of Saint Anthony Park Congregational Church, Saint Paul, Minnesota (where a memorial service was held for him on May 26, 1976).

Dr. Parham's research interests included the syntheses of hetero-cyclic compounds, including new sulfur-containing ring systems, the chemistry of divalent sulfur, bisalkylating agents, carbenes leading to dihalocylopropanes, and the use of dihalocyclopropanes in preparation of strained aromatic ring systems. He discovered the use of dihydropyran as a method of protecting hydroxyl groups in basic media and the use of dihalocarbenes in ring expansion reactions *via* 1,1-dihalocyclopropanes, a discovery which he applied extensively. He published well over 100 scientific papers. He is survived by his mother, Mrs. James Hall, and his sister, Mrs. William Kirkham, both of Dallas, Texas, his wife, Billie Lou, two daughters, Dr. Janice Jean (Mrs. Thomas A. Ophoven) and Judy (Mrs Robert Olein), and three grandchildren, all of Saint Paul, Minnesota.

We shall sorely miss this warm friend, adviser, and contributor to so much of the success of *Organic Syntheses*.

Wayland E. Noland

PREFACE

This volume of *Organic Syntheses* contains twenty-seven checked procedures of value to the modern practicing chemist. One hopes it will also serve to attract students to the charms of skillfully planned and executed experimental work. The majority of the preparations represent specific examples of important, often recently discovered synthetic methods with general applicability. As in previous volumes the preparation of a number of reagents and widely used starting materials is also included.

The preparation of 5-ACETYL-1,2,3,4,5-PENTAMETHYLCYCLO-PENTADIENE is of value in the synthesis of pentamethylcyclopentadiene and many pentamethylcyclopentadienyl metal carbonyl derivatives that are more soluble in organic solvents than those derived from cyclopentadiene. Simple preparations of 5,6-DIHYDRO-2-PYRAN-2-ONE and 2-*H*-PYRAN-2-ONE make these hitherto rather inaccessible intermediates available for cycloaddition and other reactions. The already broad scope of the Michael reaction has been widened further by including an efficient preparation of ETHYL (*E*)-3-NITROACRYLATE. Workers in the field of heterocyclic chemistry will find a simplified method for the preparation of 2,3,4,5-TETRA-HYDROPYRIDINE of help.

An increasing number of new methods are based on [2,3]-sigmatropic rearrangements. Syntheses of ETHYL 4-AMINO-3-METHYLBEN-ZOATE and ETHYL 2-METHYLINDOLE-5-CARBOXYLATE represent examples of general methods for *ortho*-ALKYLATION OF ANILINES and the preparation of INDOLES FROM ANILINES that utilize such rearrangements. The pioneering work of Merrifield has stimulated many investigations on the use of reagents made insoluble by covalent binding to a resin. I have included POLYMERIC CAR-BODIIMIDE I. PREPARATION and II. MOFFAT OXIDATION as particularly instructive and useful applications of insoluble reagents.

Despite impressive advances in the design of highly selective reagents, protection and deprotection of functional groups is still very much part of modern synthesis. The inclusion of three such techniques is thus justified. A procedure for the DEMETHYLATION OF METHYL ARYL ETHERS illustrates their facile deblocking with lithium diphenylphosphide. The reaction is specific for methyl aryl ethers, and their higher homologs remain unaffected. A wide variety of carboxylic acids, including hindered ones, can be protected in essentially quantitative yield by ESTERIFICATION WITH TRIALKYLOXONIUM SALTS. TRIFLUOROACETYLATION OF AMINES AND AMINO ACIDS UNDER NEUTRAL, MILD CONDITIONS is easily achieved in excellent yields using 1,1,1-trichloro-3,3,3-trifluoroacetone.

The search for structurally specific oxidations continues and SELECTIVE EPOXIDATION OF TERMINAL DOUBLE BONDS, CONVERSION OF NITRO TO CARBONYL BY OZONOLYSIS OF NITRONATES and ALLYLIC OXIDATION WITH HYDROGEN PEROXIDE–SELENIUM DIOXIDE illustrate some of the activities in this area.

Three of the many newly developed methods for reduction of organic compounds are covered in this volume. REDUCTIVE CLEAVAGE OF ALLYLIC ALCOHOLS, ETHERS, OR ACETATES to the thermodynamically less stable olefins is brought about by reduction with amalgamated zinc in ether containing hydrogen chloride. METHYL GROUPS BY REDUCTION OF AROMATIC CARBOXYLIC ACIDS emphasizes the reducing power of trichlorosilane, and the ENONE REDUCTION-ENOLATE ALKYLATION SEQUENCE shows how a regioselectively generated enolate can be alkylated to give a single, monosubstituted ketone of predictable structure.

New methods for the formation of carbon-carbon bonds, because of their great importance, always receive attention. Unfortunately, yields given in preliminary communications are often exaggerated and checked procedures are of special value in this area. Chapters on 3-ALKYLATED AND 3-ACYLATED INDOLES FROM A COMMON PRECURSOR, ALKYLATION OF ISOQUINOLINES via 2-BENZOYL-1,2-DIHYDROISOQUINALDONITRILES, CARBOXYLATION OF AROMATIC COMPOUNDS, CHAIN ELONGATION OF ALKENES via gem-DIHALOCYCLOPROPANES, FREE RADICAL ALKYLATION OF QUINONES, and trans-IODOPROPENYLATION OF ALKYL HALIDES contain an enormous diversity of chemistry demonstrating that boredom is far off in synthesis.

The inner salt of METHYL(CARBOXYSULFAMOYL)TRI-

ETHYLAMMONIUM HYDROXIDE converts primary alcohols to urethanes. Secondary and tertiary alcohols are dehydrated to olefins, and the reagent will undoubtedly find other uses. ACYLAMIDO-ALKYLACETOPHENONES are prepared conveniently from SUB-STITUTED PHENETHYLAMINES.

Medium-size ring ketones, first prepared in minute amounts many decades ago by Ruzicka and Stoll, have become available in quantity by RING CONTRACTION *via* FAVORSKII-TYPE REARRANGE-MENT starting with inexpensive cyclododecanone.

For the benefit of peptide chemists a section PEPTIDE SYNTHESES USING *N*-ETHYL-5-PHENYLISOXAZOLIUM-3′-SULFONATE is included. It is planned to publish a few other important methods for peptide formation as well as procedures for blocking and deblocking of functional groups found in amino acids in future volumes of *Organic Syntheses*.

The Board of Editors is grateful to the contributors of the preparations included in this volume and welcomes both the submission of preparations for future volumes and suggestions for change that will enhance the usefulness of *Organic Syntheses*. Submitters are kindly asked to examine the instructions on pages v and vi that describe the type of preparations we wish to receive and also the information to be included in each contribution. A style guide for preparing manuscripts is available from the Secretary to the Board, and submitters are requested to follow its instructions.

As in previous volumes of *Organic Syntheses* unchecked procedures are tabulated at the end of this volume. Of the preparations received between July 1, 1975 and May 15, 1976, only those that have been accepted by the Board of Editors for checking are listed. These unchecked procedures are available from the Secretary's office for a nominal fee.

The Editor-in-Chief wishes to thank a number of people for their varied contributions. My colleagues on the Board of Editors and their collaborators have checked the majority of the procedures included in this volume. I never realized how unpopular the checking of *Organic Syntheses* preparations is with graduate students and postdoctoral fellows until we started to verify a few in these laboratories. I am very grateful to my coworkers for having been willing to put aside their own research work, often for several weeks, to contribute to this and other volumes of *Organic Syntheses*. Special credit must go to Dr.

William K. Moberg for having edited all preparations. Without his help there probably would be no volume. Thanks are due also to Ms. Janice Smith and Mrs. Donna Latz for typing the manuscript. Finally, I want to express my sincere gratitude to Dr. S. Kasparek for preparing Author and Subject Indexes.

Cambridge, Massachusetts   GEORGE H. BÜCHI
July, 1976

CONTENTS

5-ACETYL-1,2,3,4,5-PENTAMETHYLCYCLOPENTADIENE

[Ethanone, 1-(1,2,3,4,5-pentamethyl-2,4-cyclopentadien-1-yl)-]

Submitted by R. B. KING, W. M. DOUGLAS,
and A. EFRATY[1]
Checked by J. X. McDERMOTT, G. M. WHITESIDES,
and G. BÜCHI

1. Procedure

*Caution! Explosive mixtures often result when peracids other than
m-chloroperbenzoic acid are used in this reaction. No such problem has ever
been encountered using m-chloroperbenzoic acid.*

A 3-l., three-necked, round-bottomed flask is fitted with a nitrogen-
inlet tube, a pressure-equalizing addition funnel, and an air-driven
stirring apparatus. After the system has been thoroughly purged with
nitrogen, it is charged with a solution of 100 g. (0.615 mole) of hexamethylbicyclo[2.2.0]hexadiene [Hexamethyldewarbenzene; Bicyclo-
[2.2.0]hexa-2,5-diene, 1,2,3,4,5,6-hexamethyl-] (Note 1) in 200 ml. of
toluene. The reaction mixture is cooled to 0° with a bath of ice water and
stirred rapidly while a solution of 130 g. (0.62 mole) of 85% m-chloroperbenzoic acid [Benzenecarboperoxoic acid, 3-chloro-] (Note 2) in 1.5 l.
of chloroform is added dropwise over 3–4 hours. Throughout the addition
and for 4 hours following its completion the reaction mixture is kept at
0°, after which it is stirred at room temperature for 36 hours. The

1

white precipitate that forms during the reaction (mainly *m*-chloro-benzoic acid) is removed by filtration through a 650-ml., sintered-glass funnel (porosity 10–15 M), and the filter cake is washed with two 100-ml. portions of chloroform. Combination of the filtrates gives a chloroform–toluene solution, which is condensed on a rotary evaporator with the water bath at 35–40°. When all of the chloroform has been removed, the residual toluene solution is diluted with 500 ml. of pentane and refiltered. The filtrate is washed with four 200-ml. portions of 10% aqueous sodium hydroxide and two 250-ml. portions of water, dried over anhydrous magnesium sulfate, and evaporated to dryness on a rotary evaporator with the water bath at 50°. Traces of toluene are removed under high vacuum (0.02 mm.) at 25°, and the residue is then distilled (Note 3) at 4 mm. Collection of material boiling between 72° and 95° gives about 50 g. of crude product, which is further purified by dissolving it in 50 ml. of pentane and cooling the pentane solution at −78° for several hours. The resulting white crystals are collected by filtration and dried to give 31.3–37.5 g. (29–34%) of pure 5-acetyl-1,2,3,4,5-pentamethylcyclopentadiene, m.p. 54–56° (Notes 4 and 5).

2. Notes

1. Hexamethylbicyclo[2.2.0]hexadiene may be purchased from Columbia Organic Chemicals, Columbia, South Carolina, or Henley Chemical Company, New York, New York. The cost at the time of submission was approximately $150 per 200 g.

2. *m*-Chloroperbenzoic acid may be purchased from Columbia Organic Chemicals or the Aldrich Chemical Company, Inc., Milwaukee, Wisconsin.

3. Distillation was performed using a 30-cm. vacuum-jacketed column wrapped with heating tape and containing a spiral of wire (Nichrome or Chromel) in the center bore. The receiver portion of the assembly contained two flasks, one to collect the material that distilled below 72° and another for the desired fraction. An air-cooled condenser was used with this apparatus, since water cooling often causes the product to solidify and clog the condenser tube.

4. If the product is to be used for the preparation of metal carbonyl derivatives, further usable material may be obtained from the mother liquors. Removal of pentane on a rotary evaporator leaves a yellow–orange, viscous oil that is suitable for most preparative purposes.

If an extremely pure product is required, the crystalline material can be sublimed at 35–40° (0.01 mm.).

5. Infrared (C_6H_{12}) cm.$^{-1}$: 1703, 1340, 1190, 1090, 960, 760; proton magnetic resonance (CCl_4) δ, number of protons, multiplicity: 1.0 (3, singlet), 1.5 (3, singlet), 1.7 (6, singlet), 1.9 (6, singlet).

3. Discussion

The present preparation of 5-acetyl-1,2,3,4,5-pentamethylcyclopentadiene is more reliable and convenient than that previously available.[2] This compound has been used to prepare many pentamethylcyclopentadienyl metal carbonyl derivatives[3] and is also a convenient source of pentamethylcyclopentadiene for use in preparing other $(Me_5Cp)_mML_n$ derivatives.[4,5]

1. Department of Chemistry, University of Georgia, Athens, Georgia 30601.
2. H. N. Junker, W. Schafer, and H. Niedenbruck, *Chem. Ber.*, **100**, 2508 (1967).
3. R. B. King and A. Efraty, *J. Amer. Chem. Soc.*, **94**, 3773 (1972).
4. R. B. King and M. Bisnette, *J. Organometal. Chem.*, **8**, 287 (1967).
5. U. Burger, A. Delay, and F. Mazenod, *Helv. Chim. Acta*, **57**, 2106 (1974); D. Feitler and G. M. Whitesides, *Inorg. Chem.*, **15**, 466 (1976).

ACYLAMIDOALKYL ACETOPHENONES FROM SUBSTITUTED PHENETHYLAMINES: 2-(2-ACETAMIDOETHYL)-4,5-DIMETHOXYACETOPHENONE

[Acetamide, *N*-[2-(2-acetyl-4,5-dimethoxyphenyl)ethyl]-]

Submitted by A. BROSSI, L. A. DOLAN, and S. TEITEL[1]
Checked by HIROSHI ITAZAKI and WATARU NAGATA

1. Procedure

Caution! Part A should be conducted in a hood to avoid inhalation of hydrogen chloride fumes.

A. 6,7-*Dimethoxy-1-methyl-3,4-dihydroisoquinoline* [*Isoquinoline, 3,4-dihydro-6,7-dimethoxy-1-methyl-*]. A 2-l., three-necked, round-bottomed flask equipped with a mechanical stirrer, a reflux condenser protected by a calcium chloride tube, and a pressure-equalizing dropping funnel is charged with 54.0 g. (0.243 mole) of *N*-acetylhomoveratrylamine [Acetamide, *N*-[2-(3,4-dimethoxyphenyl)ethyl]-] (Note 1) and 275 ml. of dry toluene (Note 2). The mixture is stirred, warmed to 40°, and treated with 52.5 ml. (0.572 mole) (Note 3) of phosphorus oxychloride [Phosphoryl chloride] (Note 4), which is added over 1 hour (Note 5). After addition, the reaction mixture is stirred at reflux for 2 hours, then cooled with an ice bath for 4 hours. The resulting crystals are collected by filtration and dried overnight at 50° in a vacuum oven to give 79.0–79.5 g. (Note 6) of 6,7-dimethoxy-1-methyl-3,4-dihydroisoquinoline dichlorophosphate, m.p. 148–152° (Note 7). This material is dissolved in 150 ml. of water (Note 8), and the solution is basified with 100 ml. of aqueous 40% sodium hydroxide (Note 9). The oil which separates is drawn off, and the aqueous solution is washed with three 20-ml. portions of chloroform. These extracts and the oil are combined, washed with 15 ml. of water, and dried over anhydrous sodium sulfate. Removal of chloroform using a rotary evaporator provides a product weighing 47.0–48.0 g. (95–96%), which is used without purification in Part B (Note 10).

B. 2-*Acetyl-6,7-dimethoxy-1-methylene-1,2,3,4-tetrahydroisoquinoline* [*Isoquinoline, 2-acetyl-1,2,3,4-tetrahydro-6,7-dimethoxy-1-methylene-*]. A 1-l., three-necked, round-bottomed flask equipped with a mechanical stirrer, a reflux condenser topped with a calcium chloride drying tube, and a thermometer is charged with 110 ml. of acetic anhydride, 110 ml. of pyridine, and 45.0 g. (0.22 mole) of the dihydroisoquinoline prepared in Part A. The reaction mixture is stirred and heated at 90–95° for 30 minutes, stored at room temperature overnight, and concentrated by distillation at 50° using a rotary evaporator. The residue is diluted with 20 ml. of ethyl acetate, and another evaporation under reduced pressure gives material that can be crystallized from 75 ml. of ethyl acetate to yield 38.5–41.0 g. (72–77%) of product, m.p. 106–107° (Note 11).

C. 2-(2-*Acetamidoethyl*)-4,5-*dimethoxyacetophenone*. A slurry of 31.0 g. (0.125 mole) of the methylene derivative obtained in Part B and

75 ml. of aqueous 5% hydrochloric acid is stirred and warmed on a steam bath to 60–65°. As soon as all the solid has dissolved, the solution is cooled with an ice bath to 30° and basified by slowly adding a solution of 6.25 g. of potassium carbonate in 12.5 ml. of water (Note 12). The crystalline precipitate is collected by filtration, washed with three 12.5-ml. portions of water, and air-dried to provide 30.5–32.0 g. (91–93%) of the acetophenone, m.p. 123–125° (Note 13).

2. Notes

1. *N*-Acetylhomoveratrylamine[2] is prepared by adding 190 ml. of acetic anhydride to a stirred solution of 300 g. (1.80 moles) of β-(3,4-dimethoxyphenyl)ethylamine [Benzeneethanamine, 3,4-dimethoxy-] (Aldrich Chemical Company, Inc.) in 150 ml. of pyridine at such a rate that the temperature is maintained at 90–95° (*ca.* 1.5 hours is required). After the solution has been stored at room temperature overnight, the volatile material is evaporated under reduced pressure, and the residue is crystallized from ethyl acetate to give 286–306 g. (78–83%) of acetylated product, m.p. 99–100°.

2. The checkers used reagent-grade toluene dried over Linde type 5A molecular sieves.

3. The checkers obtained an identical result when the molar ratio of phosphorous oxychloride to substrate was reduced from 2.35 to 1.5.

4. The checkers obtained phosphorus oxychloride from Wako Pure Chemical Industries, Ltd., Japan and distilled it prior to use.

5. The reaction temperature increases gradually to reflux, at which time the rate of addition is adjusted to maintain reflux.

6. This weight varies with the amount of solvent remaining.

7. Analysis calculated for $C_{12}H_{15}O_2N \cdot HOPOCl_2$: C, 42.37; H, 4.74; N, 4.12; Cl, 20.85; P, 9.10. Found: C, 42.30; H, 4.92; N, 4.21; Cl, 19.08; P, 8.51. Infrared (KBr) cm.$^{-1}$: 2800, 1665, 1602, 1565, 1105; proton magnetic resonance (D_2O) δ, number of protons, multiplicity: 3.17 (3, singlet, —N=CCH_3), 4.25 (3, singlet, OCH_3), 4.30 (3, singlet, OCH_3), 7.37 (1, singlet, aryl CH), 7.62 (1, singlet, aryl CH).

The submitters, working on a kilogram scale without purification of reagent or solvent and with no precaution against moisture, obtained 6,7-dimethoxy-1-methyl-3,4-dihydroisoquinoline hydrochloride,[2] m.p. 202–203°, instead of the dichlorophosphate at this stage. The checkers obtained this hydrochloride by either treating the free base with hydrochloric acid or recrystallizing the dichlorophosphate from methanol–ethyl acetate.

8. The crystals dissolve gradually in water and, since dissolution is exothermic due to decomposition of the dichlorophosphoric acid, ice cooling is desirable.

9. Ice is added during neutralization to keep the temperature below 30°.

10. A pure sample may be prepared by crystallization from ether: m.p. 105–107°; ultraviolet (ethanol) nm. max. (ϵ): 227 (24,000), 270 (7360), 307 (6640); ultraviolet (0.01N aqueous hydrochloric acid) nm. max. (ϵ): 244 (17,250), 302 (8740), 352 (8440); infrared (KBr) cm.$^{-1}$: 1650 (C=N).

11. Ultraviolet (ethanol) nm. max. (ϵ): 220 (30,750), 267 (13,200), 304 (7080); ultraviolet (0.01N aqueous hydrochloric acid) nm. max. (ϵ): 232 (23,500), 276 (9345), 305 (6120); infrared (KBr) cm.$^{-1}$: 880–910 (C=CH$_2$). A dimorphic form melts at 100–102°. A mixture of this material and the 6,7-dimethoxy-1-methyl-3,4-dihydroisoquinoline described in Note 10 melted below 90°.

12. The rate of addition is dependent on the amount of foaming. Ice is added periodically to keep the temperature below 35°.

13. The product can be used without further purification. Recrystallization from water gave an analytical specimen, m.p. 126–127°; ultraviolet (95% ethanol) nm. max. (ϵ): 231 (24,100), 274 (8750), 304 (5500); infrared (KBr) cm.$^{-1}$: 1673, 1633; proton magnetic resonance (CDCl$_3$) δ, number of protons, multiplicity: 1.92 (3, singlet, Ha), 2.60 (3, singlet, Hb), 3.93 (6, singlet, Hc and Hd), 6.80 (1, singlet, He), 7.22 (1, singlet, Hf), 2.68–3.17 (2, multiplet, Hg), 3.30–3.68 (2, multiplet, Hh), 6.68–7.07 (1, broad, Hi).

3. Discussion

This procedure provides a facile method for converting substituted 1-methyl-3,4-dihydroisoquinolines into the corresponding 2-(2-acetamidoethyl)acetophenones, which are useful intermediates in the synthesis of 1-(substituted phenethyl)-2-methyl-1,2,3,4-tetrahydroisoquinolines.[3,4] The sequence is uncomplicated and affords, in excellent yield, a product that requires no further purification. In addition to the examples in Table I, this method has been utilized for the synthesis of other substituted acetophenones,[3,5,6] as well as related benzophenones and a heptanophenone.[7] The latter two classes of compounds have also been obtained by ring opening of 2-ethyl-1-phenyl- or 2-ethyl-1-hexyl-6,7-dialkoxy-3,4-dihydroisoquinolinium iodides with benzoyl chloride.[8]

TABLE I

Substituted Acetamidoethyl Acetophenones[5]

R_1 R_2 — ... NH—COCH$_3$ R_3 CO CH$_3$	Melting Point	Ultraviolet (ethanol) nm. max. (ϵ)
$R_1 = OCH_3$, $R_2 = R_3 = H$	86°	221 (14,700), 269 (13,600)
R_1, $R_2 = OCH_2O$, $R_3 = H$	120°	230 (36,500), 273 (5200), 307 (5460)
$R_1 = R_2 = R_3 = OCH_3$	58°	222 (14,700), 263 (16,250)

1. Chemical Research Department, Hoffmann-La Roche Inc., Nutley, New Jersey 07110.
2. E. Späth and N. Polgar, *Monatsh. Chem.*, **51**, 190 (1929).
3. A. Brossi, H. Besendorf, B. Pellmont, M. Walter, and O. Schnider, *Helv. Chim. Acta,* **43**, 1459 (1960).
4. A. Brossi, H. Besendorf, L. A. Pirk, and A. Rheiner, Jr., in G. DeStevens, ed., "Analgetics," Academic Press, Inc., New York, N.Y., 1965, pp. 287–289.
5. A. Brossi, J. Würsch, and O. Schnider, *Chimia*, **12**, 114 (1958).
6. G. Dietz, G. Faust, and W. Fiedler, *Pharmazie*, **26**, 586 (1971).
7. J. Gardent, *C.R.H. Acad. Sci.*, **247**, 2010 (1958).
8. J. Gardent, *Bull. Soc. Chim. Fr.*, **10**, 1260 (1957).

3-ALKYLATED AND 3-ACYLATED INDOLES FROM A COMMON PRECURSOR: 3-BENZYLINDOLE AND 3-BENZOYLINDOLE

[1H-Indole, 3-(phenylmethyl)- and Methanone, 1H-indol-3-ylphenyl-]

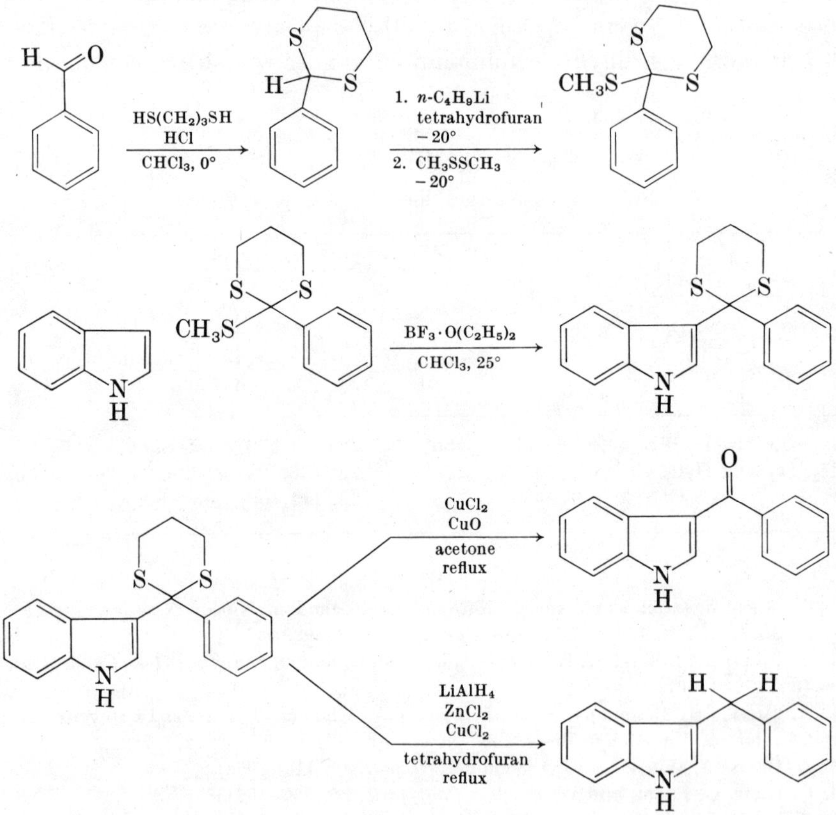

Submitted by P. STÜTZ and P. A. STADLER[1]
Checked by M. CUSHMAN and G. BÜCHI

1. Procedure

Caution! The following reactions should be conducted in a well-ventilated hood, since in each step evil-smelling sulfur compounds are either used as starting materials or generated during the reaction.

8

A. *2-Phenyl-1,3-dithiane* [*1,3-Dithiane, 2-phenyl-*]. A 100-ml., two-necked, round-bottomed flask fitted with a gas-inlet tube and a drying tube containing glass wool is charged with 5.52 g. (5.28 ml., 0.052 mole) of benzaldehyde, 5.6 g. (5.2 ml., 0.052 mole) of 1,3-propanedithiol, and 30 ml. of chloroform (Note 1). The flask is immersed in an ice bath, and a slow stream of hydrogen chloride gas is bubbled through the solution. When saturated (after *ca.* 5 minutes), the reaction mixture is left at room temperature for 30 minutes, then evaporated at reduced pressure. The oily residue (Note 2) is taken up in 50 ml. of methanol and vigorously agitated to induce crystallization. The crystals are collected by filtration, washed with ligroin, and air dried. By condensing the mother liquors, two more crops may be obtained, giving a total of 9.5–9.7 g. (93–95%) of 2-phenyl-1,3-dithiane, m.p. 69–70° (Note 3).

B. *2-Methylthio-2-phenyl-1,3-dithiane* [*1,3-Dithiane, 2-(methylthio)-2-phenyl-*]. A 2-l., three-necked, round-bottomed flask is fitted with a mechanical stirrer, a gas inlet connected to a nitrogen source, and a pressure-equalizing dropping funnel. The apparatus is maintained under a positive pressure of nitrogen and carefully protected from moisture throughout the ensuing reaction. The flask is charged with 37.2 g. (0.190 mole) of 2-phenyl-1,3-dithiane and 600 ml. of anhydrous tetrahydrofuran, and 0.228 mole of *n*-butyllithium in hexane (Note 4) is placed in the funnel. Stirring is begun, the flask is cooled with a − 20° bath, and the butyllithium solution is run into the flask over a 10-minute period. Stirring and cooling are continued for 2 hours, after which a solution of 32.2 g. (30.4 ml., 0.342 mole) of dimethyl disulfide [Disulfide, dimethyl] (Note 5) in 50 ml. of anhydrous tetrahydrofuran is added over a 10-minute period. The cooling bath is then removed, and as the solution is stirred at room temperature a fine, white precipitate forms.

When the reaction mixture has been at room temperature for 90 minutes, 300 ml. of saturated aqueous sodium chloride is added slowly, followed by 500 ml. of chloroform. The resulting aqueous layer is separated and washed with three 100-ml. portions of chloroform, and the combined chloroform solutions are dried with sodium sulfate and decolorized with activated carbon. Removal of chloroform with a rotary evaporator leaves an oily residue, which is readily crystallized from 100 ml. of methanol. The colorless crystals are collected by filtration and washed with petroleum ether to give 33.5–35.3 g. (72–77%) of 2-methylthio-2-phenyl-1,3-dithiane, m.p. 76–78°. A second crop of crystalline product may be obtained from the mother liquors.

C. 3-(2-*Phenyl*-1,3-*dithian*-2-*yl*)*indole*   [1*H*-*Indole*,   3-(2-*phenyl*-1,3-*dithian*-2-*yl*)-].   A solution of 24.2 g. (0.10 mole) of 2-methylthio-2-phenyl-1,3-dithiane and 5.86 g. (0.050 mole) of indole [1*H*-Indole] in 600 ml. of chloroform is placed in a 2-l., three-necked flask fitted with a mechanical stirrer and a 100-ml., pressure-equalizing dropping funnel. The reaction mixture is stirred vigorously, and a solution of 25 ml. (about 0.2 mole) of boron trifluoride etherate [Borane, trifluoro, compd. with 1,1'-oxybis[ethane](1:1)] (Note 6) in 50 ml. of chloroform is added over 10 minutes. An orange–brown, resinous precipitate forms as the slightly exothermic reaction proceeds. After a further 10 minutes of stirring, a solution of 5.86 g. (0.050 mole) of indole in 50 ml. of chloroform is added in one portion.

Stirring is continued for 2 hours at room temperature, and then methanol is added until a clear solution is obtained (*ca.* 10 ml. of methanol is required, and some heat is generated). When the solution has cooled, it is washed successively with 200 ml. of aqueous 2*N* potassium carbonate and 200 ml. of water. The aqueous phases are combined, washed with three 100-ml. portions of chloroform, and discarded. The organic phases are then combined, dried over sodium sulfate, and decolorized with activated carbon. Concentration of the chloroform solution thus obtained provides three crops of pale yellow crystals, which are washed with 30% hexane in chloroform and dried for 2 hours at 80°/0.1 mm. The total yield of 3-(2-phenyl-1,3-dithian-2-yl)indole is 22.3–25.4 g. (72–81%), m.p. 167–169° (Note 7). This material requires no further purification for use in Parts D or E.

D. 3-*Benzoylindole*. A 100-ml., three-necked flask fitted with a magnetic stirring bar, a condenser, and a pressure-equalizing dropping funnel is charged with 0.48 g. (0.0060 mole) of cupric oxide [Copper oxide (CuO)], 1.61 g. (0.012 mole) of anhydrous cupric chloride [copper chloride ($CuCl_2$)] (Note 8), and 40 ml. of acetone. The resulting suspension is brought to reflux with vigorous stirring, and a solution of 1.55 g. (0.0050 mole) of 3-(2-phenyl-1,3-dithian-2-yl)indole in 9 ml. of acetone and 1 ml. of *N*,*N*-dimethylformamide is added over 5 minutes. Reflux is maintained for 90 minutes, during which time the reaction mixture gradually turns yellow, and then the mixture is cooled and filtered. The insoluble material is washed with three 20-ml. portions of hot 10% ethanol in dichloromethane, and the combined organic solutions are washed with 50 ml. of aqueous 2*N* sodium carbonate (Note 9), dried over sodium sulfate, and filtered. Concentration of the filtrate to a small volume under reduced pressure gives a residue which gradually deposits crystals. Filtration provides 0.94–0.97 g. (85–88%) of pure 3-benzoylindole, m.p. 238–240°.

E. *3-Benzylindole*. A suspension of 1.34 g. (0.010 mole) of anhydrous cupric chloride (Note 8) and 2.72 g. (0.020 mole) of anhydrous zinc chloride (Note 10) in 150 ml. of anhydrous tetrahydrofuran is prepared in a 500-ml., three-necked, round-bottomed flask fitted with a mechanical stirrer and a condenser connected to a nitrogen source. This mixture is stirred at room temperature and maintained under a nitrogen atmosphere while 3.04 g. (0.080 mole) of lithium aluminum hydride [Aluminate(1 −), tetrahydro-, lithium, (*T*-4)-] is added cautiously in small portions (Note 11). The resulting exothermic reaction gives a black precipitate, which is stirred at room temperature for 45 minutes, and then 1.55 g. (0.0050 mole) of 3-(2-phenyl-1,3-dithian-2-yl)indole is added. Stirring is continued as the mixture is refluxed for 1 hour, cooled to room temperature, and quenched by very careful dropwise addition of 10 ml. of water. The resulting slurry is diluted with 100 ml. of dichloromethane and filtered to remove inorganic salts, which are washed by digesting with three 50-ml. portions of refluxing dichloromethane. The combined filtrates are then washed with a solution of 4.0 g. (0.012 mole) of mercuric acetate [Acetic acid, mercury(2 +) salt] in 100 ml. of water, dried over sodium sulfate, filtered, and concentrated on a rotary evaporator to leave about 1.1 g. of a yellow crystalline residue. Bulb-to-bulb distillation at 145–155° (0.1 mm.) provides 0.74–0.85 g. (72–82%) of practically pure 3-benzylindole as pale yellow crystals, m.p. 102–105° (Note 12).

2. Notes

1. Benzaldehyde and 1,3-propanedithiol were purchased from the Aldrich Chemical Company, Inc. and used without further purification. Exclusion of moisture during the reaction is advantageous but not essential.

2. The checkers obtained a crystalline residue, which was triturated with 10 ml. of methanol and filtered.

3. The method used is quite general for substituted 1,3-dithianes.[2] A different method is required for the preparation of 1,3-dithiane itself [see E. J. Corey and D. Seebach, *Org. Syn.*, **50**, 72 (1970)].

4. The volume of solution required will depend on the concentration

of n-butyllithium, which should be determined by titration prior to use. A convenient procedure utilizes 1,10-phenanthroline as an indicator; titration to the colorless end point with sec-butanol in xylene gives organolithium concentration directly.[3] A method for transferring large volumes of n-butyllithium solution is outlined in *Org. Syn.*, **50**, 105 (1970).

5. Dimethyl disulfide was obtained from the Aldrich Chemical Company, Inc. and used without further purification. The molar ratio used is the same as that in the original reference.[4]

6. Boron trifluoride etherate was purchased from either Fluka AG, Switzerland or Aldrich Chemical Company, Inc. The checkers distilled the commercial material from calcium hydride immediately prior to use.[5]

7. Proton magnetic resonance ($CDCl_3$) δ, number of protons, multiplicity, coupling constant J in Hz.: 1.5–2.2 (2, multiplet), 2.7–3.0 (4, multiplet), 7.0 (1, doublet, $J = 2.5$), 7.1–7.5 (6, multiplet), 7.7–8.2 (4, multiplet). A sample recrystallized from methanol–chloroform melted at 183–185°. The submitters also obtained pure product, m.p. 181–183°, after chromatography on basic alumina with 20% petroleum ether in dichloromethane as eluent.

8. Anhydrous cupric chloride was prepared by heating the dihydrate at 110° overnight.

9. This extraction must be performed gently, since violent agitation will give an emulsion.

10. Reagent-grade anhydrous zinc chloride was obtained from Merck & Company, Inc.

11. Lithium aluminum hydride was obtained from Fluka AG or from Ventron Corporation. One convenient technique for the addition is to weigh the reagent into an Erlenmeyer flask, which is then connected to the reaction flask by a short piece of Gooch tubing. In this way the solid can be added in portions without exposing it to the atmosphere.

12. Various melting points are reported in the literature for 3-benzylindole: 96–98°,[6] 103°, and 107°.[7]

3. Discussion

There are other convenient methods for the preparation of 3-benzylindole[6,7] and 3-benzoylindole.[8] The present procedure, however, has two useful elements of flexibility: it produces both 3-alkyl- and

3-acylindoles from a single precursor, and it tolerates the presence of a wide variety of substituents.

The pivotal step in this sequence is an electrophilic substitution on indole. Although the use of 1,3-dithian-2-yl carbanions is well documented, it has been shown only recently that 1,3-dithian-2-yl carbenium ions can be used in a Friedel-Crafts type reaction. This was accomplished initially using 2-methoxy-1,3-dithiane [1,3-Dithiane, 2-methoxy-] or 2-methoxy-1,3-dithiolane [1,3-Dithiolane, 2-methoxy-] and titanium tetrachloride [Titanate(1 −), tetrachloro-] as the Lewis acid catalyst.[9] 2-Substituted lysergic acid derivatives and 3-substituted indoles have been prepared under these conditions, but the method is limited in scope by the difficulties of preparing substituted 2-methoxy-1,3-dithianes. 1,3-Dithian-2-yl carbenium ions have also been prepared by protonation of ketene dithioacetals with trifluoroacetic acid,[10] but this reaction cannot be used to introduce 1,3-dithiane moieties into indole.

The procedure described herein is fairly general for indoles, and since 2-methylthio-1,3-dithianes are readily available,[2,4] it should prove versatile. Two further examples are as follows:

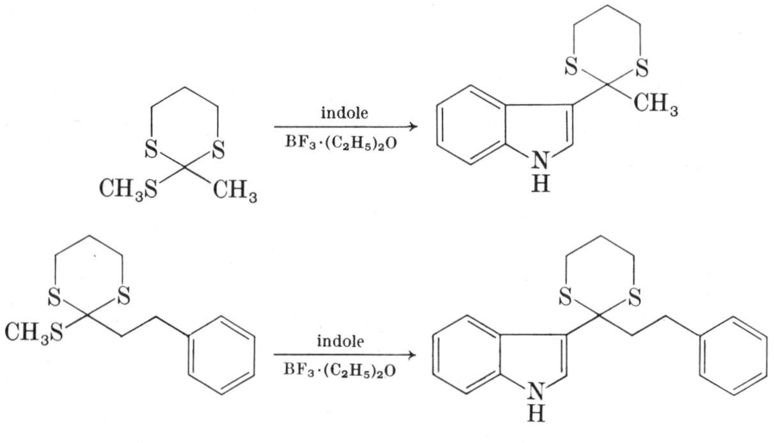

In attempting to extend the method to other activated aromatics, it was found that pyrroles give mixtures of 2- and 3-substituted products, and that naphthol ethers and benzo[b]thiophene fail to react.

The hydrolytic step (Part D) uses conditions described by Narasaka, Sakashita, and Mukaiyama.[11] It was necessary to modify the original stoichiometry, since the recommended molar ratio of substrate:cupric chloride:cupric oxide (1:2:4) gave only a 57% yield of 3-benzoylindole.

The more generally known mercuric oxide–mercuric chloride hydrolysis[2] may also be used, and in the present case it gives a yield of about 90%. The reductive desulfurization of Part E is also based on the work of Mukaiyama.[12] It is clearly superior to Raney nickel desulfurization, which gives only 35–45% of 3-benzylindole.

1. Sandoz Ltd., Pharmaceutical Division, Chemical Research, Basel, Switzerland.
2. D. Seebach, *Angew. Chem. Int. Ed. Engl.*, **6**, 442 (1967); D. Seebach, B. W. Erickson, and G. Singh, *J. Org. Chem.*, **31**, 4303 (1966).
3. S. C. Watson and J. F. Eastham, *J. Organometal. Chem.*, **9**, 165 (1967).
4. R. A. Ellison, W. D. Woessner, and C. C. Williams, *J. Org. Chem.*, **37**, 2757 (1972).
5. G. Zweifel and H. C. Brown, *Org. React.*, **13**, 28 (1963).
6. H. Plieninger, *Chem. Ber.*, **87**, 127 (1954).
7. R. Cornforth and R. Robinson, *J. Chem. Soc. London*, 680 (1942).
8. W. C. Anthony, *J. Org. Chem.*, **25**, 2049 (1960).
9. P. Stütz and P. A. Stadler, *Helv. Chim. Acta*, **55**, 75 (1972).
10. F. A. Carey and A. S. Court, *J. Org. Chem.*, **37**, 1926 (1972).
11. K. Narasaka, T. Sakashita, and T. Mukaiyama, *Bull. Chem. Soc. Jap.*, **45**, 3724 (1972).
12. T. Mukaiyama, *Int. J. Sulfur Chem.*, **7**, 173 (1972).

ortho-ALKYLATION OF ANILINES:
ETHYL 4-AMINO-3-METHYLBENZOATE

[Benzoic acid, 4-amino-3-methyl-, ethyl ester]

Submitted by P. G. Gassman and G. Gruetzmacher[1]
Checked by M. Savitsky, R. R. Schmidt, III,
and G. Büchi

1. Procedure

Caution! Part A must be conducted in a hood due to the noxious odor of dimethyl sulfide. In Part B, the usual precautions associated with the pyrophoric reagent Raney nickel must be observed (see Note 8).

A. *Ethyl 4-Amino-3-(methylthiomethyl)benzoate* [*Benzoic acid, 4-amino-3-[(methylthio)methyl]-*]. A 1-l., three-necked, round-bottomed flask is fitted with a mechanical stirrer, a condenser topped with a gas-inlet tube, and a two-necked adapter holding a low-temperature thermometer and a 100-ml., pressure-equalizing dropping funnel. The flask is charged with 16.50 g. (0.10 mole) of ethyl *p*-aminobenzoate [Benzocaine; Benzoic acid, 4-amino-, ethyl ester] (Note 1), 300 ml. of acetonitrile, and 100 ml. of dichloromethane, is flushed with nitrogen, and is then immersed in a 40% aqueous methanol–dry ice bath maintained between

15

$-40°$ and $-50°$ (Note 2). When the reaction mixture has come to $-40°$, a solution of 10.85 g. (0.10 mole) of *tert*-butyl hypochlorite[2] [Hypochlorous acid, 1,1-dimethylethyl ester] in 25 ml. of dichloromethane is added dropwise over a 15-minute period. The addition funnel is rinsed with 25 ml. of dichloromethane, the reaction solution is stirred for another 5 minutes, and then 25 ml. (*ca.* 0.3 mole) of dimethyl sulfide [Methane, thiobis-] (Note 3) is added at a rate that allows the vigorously stirred reaction mixture to be maintained below $-30°$.

Shortly after the addition is complete, a voluminous white precipitate appears, and the resulting slurry is stirred and maintained at $-50°$ to $-40°$ for 4 hours. Cooling and stirring are continued as 25 ml. (0.18 mole) of triethylamine [Ethanamine, N,N-diethyl] (Note 4) is added dropwise, during which time the reaction mixture first goes to a clear solution and then becomes cloudy. The resulting mixture is stirred at $-50°$ to $-40°$ for 1 hour.

The cooling bath is then replaced by a steam bath, and the reaction mixture is refluxed for 16 hours. It is then cooled, transferred to a one-necked, 1-l., round-bottomed flask, and concentrated to dryness on a rotary evaporator. The dark residue is dissolved in a mixture of 200 ml. of water, 200 ml. of dichloromethane, and 20 ml. of triethylamine, and the aqueous phase is separated and washed with two 200-ml. portions of dichloromethane. The organic phases are combined and washed with 300 ml. of saturated aqueous sodium chloride, dried over anhydrous magnesium sulfate, and filtered. Removal of the solvent on a rotary evaporator gives a red oil, which solidifies on storage at 0–5° (Note 5). Recrystallization of this solid from 40 ml. of absolute ethanol gives 7.6–8.4 g. (34–37%) of ethyl 4-amino-3-(methylthiomethyl)-benzoate, m.p. 83–85°. A second crop of 1.1–2.5 g. of crystalline material, m.p. 78–83°, may be obtained by concentration of the mother liquors (Note 6).

B. *Ethyl 4-Amino-3-methylbenzoate.* A 1-l., three-necked, round-bottomed flask equipped with a mechanical stirrer, a condenser, and a nitrogen-inlet tube is charged with 11.25 g. (0.050 mole) of ethyl 4-amino-3-(methylthiomethyl)benzoate, 300 ml. of absolute ethanol, and 17 teaspoons (*ca.* 50 g.) of W-2 Raney nickel (Note 7). The reaction mixture is stirred at 25° for one hour, then stirring is discontinued, and the ethanolic solution is decanted from the catalyst (Note 8). The catalyst is then washed with one 300-ml. portion of absolute ethanol and one 500-ml. portion of dichloromethane, the solvent being removed by decanting in each case. Combination of the organic solutions and concentration on a rotary evaporator gives a solid which is dissolved in 200 ml. of dichloromethane. This solution is dried over anhydrous magnesium sulfate, filtered, and taken to dryness on a rotary evaporator to leave 7.0–7.6 g. (77–84%) of ethyl 4-amino-3-methylbenzoate as a white solid, m.p. 75–78°.

2. Notes

1. Benzocaine was purchased from Mallinckrodt Chemical Works and was recrystallized from absolute ethanol prior to use to give material of m.p. 91–92°.

2. Fairly precise temperature control is required, since the reaction mixture begins to solidify at about −50°.

3. Dimethyl sulfide was purchased from MC and B Manufacturing Chemists and used without further purification.

4. Triethylamine was purchased from the J. T. Baker Chemical Company and used without further purification.

5. Solidification is facilitated by dissolving the oil in a minimum amount of ether (ca. 100 ml.) and removing the ether on a rotary evaporator. Should the oil still refuse to solidify, this process is repeated several times with pentane.

6. The second crop of crystalline material is contaminated with a small amount of ethyl p-aminobenzoate and is usually red–orange in color. It is of sufficient purity to be used in Part B.

7. W-2 Raney nickel was purchased from W. R. Grace & Company. Prior to use it was washed with distilled water until the washings were neutral, then washed three times with absolute ethanol and stored under ethanol until needed.[3]

8. Activated Raney nickel is pyrophoric and should never be allowed to become dry. Thus decanting is preferred to filtration, and when decanting, a small amount of solvent must always be left behind to cover the catalyst powder. For safe disposal, the spent catalyst should be slurried in water and flushed down the drain under running water.

3. Discussion

This procedure illustrates a general method for the ortho-alkylation of anilines.[4] It can be utilized for both anilines and mono-N-substituted anilines, and a variety of functional groups can be tolerated on the aromatic ring. By substituting α-thioketones and α-thioesters for dialkyl sulfides, the method has been extended to produce indoles[5] and oxindoles,[6] respectively. An example of the indole synthesis appears elsewhere in this volume.

Ethyl 4-amino-3-methylbenzoate has been reported previously.[7]

1. Department of Chemistry, The Ohio State University, Columbus, Ohio 43210.
2. M. J. Mintz and C. Walling, *Org. Syn.*, **49**, 9 (1969).
3. R. Mozingo, *Org. Syn.*, Coll. Vol. **3**, 181 (1955).
4. P. G. Gassman and G. Gruetzmacher, *J. Amer. Chem. Soc.*, **95**, 588 (1973).
5. P. G. Gassman and T. J. van Bergen, *J. Amer. Chem. Soc.*, **95**, 590 (1973).
6. P. G. Gassman and T. J. van Bergen, *J. Amer. Chem. Soc.*, **95**, 2718 (1973).
7. F. J. Viliani, U.S. Patent 2,764,519 (1956) [*C.A.*, **51**, 4443e (1957)].

ALKYLATION OF ISOQUINOLINES
via 2-BENZOYL-1,2-DIHYDROISOQUINALDONITRILES:
1-BENZYLISOQUINOLINE

[Isoquinoline, 1-(phenylmethyl)-]

Submitted by BARRIE C. UFF,[1] JOHN R. KERSHAW,[1]
and JOHN L. NEUMEYER[2]
Checked by A. BROSSI, H. BRUDERER,
and J. METZGER

1. Procedure

Caution! This reaction involves highly toxic cyanide salts. It may be carried out safely, however, if prudent laboratory procedures are practiced. In particular, cyanide residues should be collected and disposed of separately (Note 1), and the entire sequence should be performed in an efficient hood.

A. *2-Benzoyl-1,2-dihydroisoquinaldonitrile* [1-*Isoquinolinecarbonitrile, 2-benzoyl-1,2-dihydro-*]. A 1-l., three-necked, round-bottomed flask

19

fitted with a mechanical stirrer, a thermometer, and a 250-ml., pressure-equalizing dropping funnel is charged with 64.6 g. (0.50 mole) of freshly distilled isoquinoline (Note 2) in 400 ml. of dichloromethane and 97.7 g. (1.5 moles) of potassium cyanide (Note 2) in 200 ml. of water. The mixture is stirred vigorously as 126.5 g. (121 ml., 1.0 mole) of freshly distilled benzoyl chloride is added from the dropping funnel over 1 hour. As the addition proceeds, the temperature rises to 38°, and the dichloro-methane comes to reflux. Stirring is continued for an additional 3 hours, and the resulting brown reaction mixture is filtered through 20 g. of Dicalite Speedex. After the insoluble material has been washed with 200 ml. of water and 200 ml. of dichloromethane, the filtrate and washings are transferred to a separatory funnel. The layers are separated (Notes 1 and 3), and the dichloromethane layer is washed successively with 300 ml. of water, three 200-ml. portions of aqueous $2N$ hydrochloric acid, 200 ml. of water, three 200-ml. portions of aqueous $2N$ sodium hydroxide, and 200 ml. of water (Note 1). After drying over anhydrous potassium carbonate, the dichloromethane solution is filtered and evaporated under reduced pressure to give 108–110 g. of a pale brown solid. This crude product is dissolved in 200 ml. of boiling ethyl acetate, and the hot solution is filtered and set aside to cool. On standing, the Reissert compound crystallizes as cream rhombs, which are collected on a Büchner funnel and dried in a vacuum desiccator to give 89.9 g. (69%) of 2-benzoyl-1,2-dihydroisoquinaldonitrile, m.p. 125–127° (Notes 4 and 5).

B. 1-*Benzylisoquinoline.* An 11.4-g. portion of 55% sodium hydride–mineral oil dispersion (Note 6) is washed free of oil by slurrying with two 40-ml. portions of dry hexane (Note 7) and decanting the liquid. The sodium hydride is then transferred to a dry, 2-l., three-necked, round-bottomed flask fitted with a mechanical stirrer, a 500-ml., pressure-equalizing dropping funnel, and a nitrogen-inlet tube (Note 8). Then 200 ml. of N,N-dimethylformamide (Note 9) is added, and the resulting slurry is cooled to −10° with a methanol–ice bath. Stirring is begun, and a solution of 65.0 g. (0.25 mole) of 2-benzoyl-1,2-dihydro-isoquinaldonitrile and 32 g. (29 ml., 0.25 mole) of benzyl chloride [Benzene, (chloromethyl)-] in 400 ml. of dry N,N-dimethylformamide is added dropwise over 1 hour. During addition the reaction mixture becomes dark and then fades to light brown. Ice is added as required to hold the bath temperature near −10° (Note 10).

When the addition is complete, the reaction mixture is stirred overnight at room temperature, still maintaining a nitrogen atmosphere. Excess sodium hydride is then destroyed by slow addition of 10 ml. of water, the N,N-dimethylformamide is evaporated at 40° (0.01 mm.), and the residue is diluted with 800 ml. of toluene and 800 ml. of water. After thorough shaking, the mixture is transferred to a separatory funnel. The aqueous layer is discarded, and the toluene layer is washed with two 200-ml. portions of water, dried over anhydrous potassium carbonate, and filtered free of drying agent. Removal of toluene under reduced pressure leaves a yellow oil, which crystallizes on standing (Note 11).

This material is dissolved in 500 ml. of ethanol, and the solution is transferred to a 2-l., round-bottomed flask. A solution of 200 g. of sodium hydroxide in 200 ml. of water is added, and the mixture is refluxed for 2 hours. Ethanol is then removed by distillation, and the residue is shaken with 500 ml. of water and 800 ml. of toluene. The toluene layer is separated, washed with two 200-ml. portions of water, and then vigorously shaken with 600 ml. of 2N aqueous hydrochloric acid. A portion of the 1-benzylisoquinoline hydrochloride precipitates at this point and is collected on a Büchner funnel and washed with 200-ml. portions of water and toluene. The filtrate is then transferred to a separatory funnel, the acidic layer is separated, and the crystals from the Büchner funnel are suspended in this layer. After basifying the suspension with 50% aqueous sodium hydroxide, the oil that separates is extracted with three 200-ml. portions of dichloromethane. The combined dichloromethane layers are dried over anhydrous potassium carbonate, filtered, and evaporated under reduced pressure to leave the crude product as a yellow oil. Distillation under reduced pressure then provides 49.8 g. (91%) of pure 1-benzylisoquinoline as a pale yellow oil, b.p. 145–150° (0.01 mm.). The product solidifies on standing and may be crystallized from chloroform–hexane to give colorless prisms, m.p. 54–55° (Note 12).

2. Notes

1. The original aqueous layer and the aqueous washings of the dichloromethane layer contain cyanide residues. These should be destroyed prior to disposal by making the solution strongly basic with sodium hydroxide and then adding, with stirring, a large excess of ferrous sulfate. The resulting suspension should be boiled for several

hours in the hood before disposal. This process converts cyanide to the nontoxic Prussian Blue (ferric ferrocyanide), which precipitates.

2. This product is supplied by Fluka AG, Buchs, Switzerland.

3. Any precipitate occurring during the washing procedure was removed by filtration through a small amount of Dicalite Speedex, obtained from Chemische Fabrik Schweizerhalle, Switzerland.

4. A further fraction of less pure material can be obtained by evaporating the filtrate to approximately 50 ml. and refrigerating the solution overnight.

5. The literature[3] gives m.p. 124–126°. Infrared (KBr) cm.$^{-1}$: 2240 very weak (—C≡N), 1658 strong (C=O), 1632 strong (C=C—N); proton magnetic resonance (8% w/w in $CDCl_3$) δ, number of protons, multiplicity, coupling constant J in Hz.: 6.06 (1, doublet, $J_{3,4}$ = 7.8, H_4), 6.57 (1, broad singlet, H_1), 6.60 (1, doublet of doublets, $J_{3,4}$ = 7.8, $J_{1,3}$ = 1, H_3), 7.0–7.7 (9, multiplet, aromatic CH).

6. This product is supplied by Fluka AG, Buchs, Switzerland. The amount of dispersion used should provide 6.25 g. (0.26 mole) of pure sodium hydride. A small molar excess is used to allow for variation in the sodium hydride:oil ratio of commercial material.

7. The hexane was dried by filtration through alumina.

8. The apparatus was dried in an oven and assembled hot under a stream of dry, oxygen-free nitrogen. A nitrogen atmosphere was maintained throughout the reaction, since oxygen reacts with the Reissert anion to give 1-cyanoisoquinoline [1-Isoquinolinecarbonitrile].[4] Commercial nitrogen was dried by bubbling through concentrated sulfuric acid. It was found to be sufficiently oxygen-free to require no special treatment.

9. N,N-Dimethylformamide was purchased from Merck, Darmstadt and dried by standing over molecular sieves (Union Carbide, type 4A).

10. It is necessary to hold the reaction temperature below −5° in order to prevent 1,2-rearrangement of the Reissert anion to 1-benzoyliso-quinoline [Isoquinoline, 1-benzoyl-].[5]

11. The intermediate 1-benzyl-2-benzoyl-1,2-dihydroisoquinaldo-

nitrile [1-Isoquinolinecarbonitrile, 2-benzoyl-1,2-dihydro-1-(phenyl-methyl)-] can be crystallized from ethyl acetate–hexane to give material melting at 130–131°. The compound has been described as an oil[5,6] and as a crystalline product, m.p. 129°.[7] Infrared (KBr) cm.$^{-1}$: 2236 weak (C$\equiv$N), 1669 strong (C$=$O), 1641 strong (C$=$C—N); proton magnetic resonance (8% w/w in CDCl$_3$) δ, number of protons, multiplicity, coupling constant J in Hz.: 3.48 and 3.78 (2, AB quartet, $J = 13$, C$_6$H$_5$CH_2—), 5.54 (1, doublet, $J = 8$, H_4), 6.37 (1, doublet, $J = 8$, H_3), 6.75–7.8 (14, multiplet, aromatic CH). Analysis calculated for C$_{24}$H$_{18}$N$_2$O: C, 82.26; H, 5.18; N, 7.99. Found: C, 82.08; H, 5.29; N, 7.89.

12. The literature gives m.p. 56°.[8] Infrared (KBr) cm.$^{-1}$: 1621, 1601, 1585, 1560, 1500, 1493; proton magnetic resonance (8% w/w in CDCl$_3$) δ, number of protons, multiplicity, coupling constant J in Hz.: 4.66 (2, singlet, CH_2), 7.1–8.25 (10, multiplet, aromatic CH), 8.5 (1, doublet, $J = 6$, H_3).

3. Discussion

Other methods for the synthesis of 1-benzylisoquinolines include: (a) dehydrogenation of 1-benzyl-3,4-dihydroisoquinolines,[9,10] which in turn are produced in the Bischler-Napieralski reaction by heating N-phenylacetyl-β-phenylethylamines with a dehydrating agent such as phosphorus pentoxide in xylene,[9,10] (b) the Pictet-Gams modification of (a), in which N-phenylacetyl-2-hydroxy-2-phenylethylamines are dehydrated with phosphorus pentoxide,[8,10,11,12] (c) thermal rearrangements of N-benzylisoquinolinium chlorides in the presence of copper,[13] and (d) addition of benzylmagnesium chloride to isoquinolines.[14] The first two methods are limited in scope by the accessibility of starting materials and the requirement that the aromatic ring carry an electron-donating substituent *para* to the point of closure for reasonable yields. The last two methods often lead to mixtures and have not been shown to be of general applicability.

The Reissert method[15]—conversion of an isoquinoline to a 2-benzoyl-1,2-dihydroisoquinaldonitrile (Reissert compound), alkylation, and hydrolysis—has enjoyed wide success in the synthesis of benzyliso-quinoline and related alkaloids.[16,17] In particular, aporphines are prepared conveniently by converting isoquinolines to 1-(o-nitrobenzyl)-isoquinolines *via* a Reissert sequence, followed by N-alkylation, reduction, and Pschorr cyclization.[17]

The present procedure illustrates two recent and highly useful modifications of the Reissert method. First, the Reissert compound is formed by the two-phase method of Popp and Blount.[18] This modification generally gives much higher yields for isoquinolines[19] and quinolines[20] than does the single (aqueous) phase method used previously,[21] succeeding in many cases where the aqueous method fails altogether. The aqueous method is generally less clean and has the disadvantage that both starting material and product are insoluble in water. A non-aqueous benzene–hydrogen cyanide method[22] has also been used for Reissert compound formation, but it has the obvious drawbacks associated with the use of hydrogen cyanide. Second, the Reissert anion is formed with sodium hydride–N,N-dimethylformamide. This modification, developed by the submitters[23] and independently by Popp and Wefer,[6,24] has several advantages over the earlier reagent, phenyllithium in ether.[5,21] The sodium hydride does not have to be specially prepared, and its strength is known without titration; cessation of hydrogen evolution indicates that carbanion generation is complete; and the use of N,N-dimethylformamide overcomes solubility problems often encountered because of the ether used in the earlier method.

1. Department of Chemistry, Loughborough University of Technology, Leicestershire, LE11 3TU, England.
2. Department of Medicinal Chemistry and Pharmacology, Northeastern University, Boston, Massachusetts 02115.
3. J. J. Padbury and H. G. Lindwall, *J. Amer. Chem. Soc.*, **67**, 1268 (1945).
4. G. W. Kirby, S. L. Tan, and B. C. Uff, International Congress of Pure and Applied Chemistry, Boston, 1971, Abstract 270, p. 113.
5. V. Boekelheide and J. Weinstock, *J. Amer. Chem. Soc.*, **74**, 660 (1952).
6. F. D. Popp and J. M. Wefer, *J. Heterocycl. Chem.*, **4**, 183 (1967).
7. M. Markosza, *Tetrahedron Lett.*, 677 (1969).
8. R. Forsyth, I. Kelly, and F. L. Pyman, *J. Chem. Soc. London*, **127**, 1659 (1925).
9. A. Pictet and F. W. Kay, *Ber.*, **42**, 1973 (1909); C. I. Brodrick and W. F. Short, *J. Chem. Soc. London*, 2587 (1949).
10. W. M. Whaley and T. R. Govindachari, *Org. React.*, **6**, 74 (1951).
11. A. Pictet and A. Gams, *Ber.*, **43**, 2384 (1910); R. Robinson, *J. Chem. Soc. London*, **95**, 2167 (1909).
12. A. Brossi and S. Teitel, *Helv. Chim. Acta*, **49**, 1757 (1966).
13. J. v. Braun, J. Nelles, and A. May, *Ber.*, **70B**, 1767 (1937).
14. E. Bergmann and W. Rosenthal, *J. Prakt. Chem.*, **135**, 267 (1932).
15. A. Reissert, *Ber.*, **38**, 3415 (1905); F. D. Popp, *Advan. Heterocycl. Chem.* **9**, 1 (1968).
16. F. D. Popp, *Heterocycles*, **1**, 165 (1973); A. H. Jackson and G. W. Stewart, *Chem. Commun.*, 149 (1971); S. F. Dyke and A. C. Ellis, *Tetrahedron*, **27**, 3083 (1971); S. F. Dyke and A. C. Ellis, *Tetrahedron*, **28**, 3999 (1972); B. C. Uff, J. R. Kershaw, and S. R. Chhabra, *J. C. S. Perkin I*, 479 (1972); A. J. Birch, A. H. Jackson, P. V. R. Shannon, and P. S. P. Varma, *Tetrahedron Lett.*, 4789 (1972); F. R. Stermitz and D. K. Williams, *J. Org. Chem.*, **38**, 1761 (1973).

17. J. L. Neumeyer, B. R. Neustadt, and J. Weintraub, *Tetrahedron Lett.*, 3107 (1967); J. L. Neumeyer, K. H. Oh, K. K. Weinhardt, and B. R. Neustadt, *J. Org. Chem.*, **34**, 3786 (1969); M. P. Cava and M. Srinivasan, *Tetrahedron*, **26**, 4649 (1970); M. P. Cava and M. V. Lakshmikantham, *J. Org. Chem.*, **35**, 1867 (1970); M. P. Cava and I. Noguchi, *J. Org. Chem.*, **37**, 2936 (1972); M. P. Cava and I. Noguchi, *J. Org. Chem.*, **38**, 60 (1973); J. L. Neumeyer, B. R. Neustadt, K. H. Oh, K. K. Weinhardt, and C. B. Boyce, *J. Med. Chem.*, **16**, 1223 (1973); J. L. Neumeyer, U.S. Patent 3,717,639 (1973).

18. F. D. Popp and W. Blount, *Chem. Ind. London*, 550 (1961).

19. F. D. Popp and W. Blount, *J. Org. Chem.*, **27**, 297 (1962).

20. F. D. Popp, W. Blount, and P. Melvin, *J. Org. Chem.*, **26**, 4930 (1961).

21. J. Weinstock and V. Boekelheide, *Org. Syn.*, **38**, 58 (1958); *Org. Syn.*, Coll. Vol. **4**, 641 (1963).

22. J. M. Grosheintz and H. O. L. Fischer, *J. Amer. Chem. Soc.*, **63**, 2021 (1941).

23. J. R. Kershaw and B. C. Uff, *Chem. Commun.*, 331 (1966); B. C. Uff and J. R. Kershaw, *J. Chem. Soc. C*, 666 (1969).

24. F. D. Popp and J. M. Wefer, *Chem. Commun.*, 207 (1966).

ALLYLIC OXIDATION WITH HYDROGEN PEROXIDE–SELENIUM DIOXIDE: *trans*-PINOCARVEOL

[Bicyclo[3.1.1]heptan-3-ol, 6,6-dimethyl-2-methylene-, (1α,3α,5α)-]

Submitted by J. M. Coxon, E. Dansted,
and M. P. Hartshorn[1]
Checked by D. W. Brooks and S. Masamune

1. Procedure

Caution! Selenium compounds are exceedingly toxic (Note 1). Hydrogen peroxide attacks the skin and may decompose violently (Note 2). The reaction should be carried out behind a safety screen and in an efficient fume hood, and the operator should wear safety glasses and rubber gloves.

A 500-ml., three-necked, round-bottomed flask is fitted with a mechanical stirrer, a thermometer, a dropping funnel, and a reflux condenser. A solution of 0.74 g. (0.007 mole) of selenium dioxide in 150 ml. of *tert*-butyl alcohol [2-Propanol, 2-methyl] is introduced into the flask, followed by 68 g. (0.50 mole) of β-pinene [Bicyclo[3.1.1]-heptane, 6,6-dimethyl-2-methylene-] (Note 3), and the resulting mixture is warmed to 40° by means of a hot water bath. Then 35 ml. (0.62 mole) of aqueous 50% hydrogen peroxide (Note 2) is added dropwise over 90 minutes, during which time the mixture is maintained at 40–50° by occasional immersion in a cold water bath. After stirring for a further 2 hours, the reaction mixture is diluted with 50 ml. of benzene, washed with three 50-ml. portions of aqueous saturated ammonium sulfate, and dried over sodium sulfate. A small amount of hydroquinone is added (Note 4), and the solvents are removed on a rotary evaporator. *trans*-Pinocarveol is isolated by simple distillation under reduced pressure, which affords 37–42 g. (49–55%), b.p. 60–70° (1 mm.), n_D^{22} 1.4972, $[\alpha]_D^{20}$ +53.5 to +60.0° (*c* 2.5, methanol) (Note 5).

2. Notes

1. The physiological properties of selenium compounds are similar to those of arsenic compounds. Any selenium dioxide solid or solution spilled on the skin should be removed immediately by washing under running water.

2. Aqueous 50% hydrogen peroxide causes immediate blistering if allowed to come into contact with the skin. The presence of metal salts may cause decomposition of the hydrogen peroxide.

3. The checkers purchased β-pinene, $[\alpha]_D^{20}$ −16.6° (*c* 1.9, methanol), from Aldrich Chemical Company, Inc.

4. Hydroquinone stabilizes the product during distillation by reducing traces of peroxide present in the reaction product.

5. Gas chromatographic analysis (capillary column coated with polypropylene glycol, 60.9 m., 100°) indicated that the product was *ca.* 95% pure (submitters). The checkers found the once-distilled material to be analytically pure. Analysis calculated for $C_{10}H_{16}O$: C, 78.90; H, 10.59. Found: C, 78.71; H, 10.55. Infrared (CCl_4) cm.$^{-1}$: 3600 medium, 3460 broad, medium, 1645 medium; proton magnetic resonance (CCl_4) δ, number of protons, multiplicity, coupling constant J in Hz.: 0.63 (3, singlet), 1.26 (3, singlet), 1.6–2.5 (6, multiplet), 2.88 (1, singlet, OH), 4.33 (1, approximate doublet, $J = 7$), 4.74 (1, approximate singlet), 4.96 (1, approximate singlet).

3. Discussion

trans-Pinocarveol is an important intermediate in the preparation of substituted pinane systems. It has been prepared by oxidation of

β-pinene with lead tetraacetate and hydrolysis of the corresponding ester in 32% yield;[2] by photosensitized oxidation of α-pinene [Bicyclo-[3.1.1]hept-2-ene, 2,6,6-trimethyl-], followed by reduction of the corresponding hydroperoxide, in 35% yield;[3] by oxidation of β-pinene with molar quantities of selenium dioxide in 53–64% yield;[4] and by epoxidation of α-pinene followed by isomerization with a variety of bases, of which lithium diethylamide (74–80% yield over the two steps) is best.[5]

The present procedure is a convenient, one-step method of preparing optically active trans-pinocarveol. Although lower in yield than the lithium diethylamide procedure, it is more readily adaptable to large-scale work. Moreover, the two methods are complimentary in the conditions required (neutral vs. basic) and in the overall transformation accomplished:

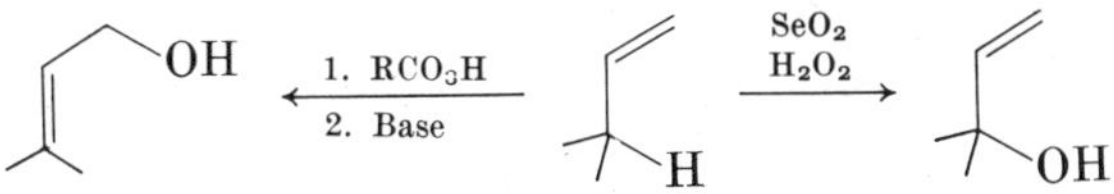

Since only catalytic quantities of selenium dioxide are required, the danger of handling large quantities of this material (Note 1) is avoided. Furthermore, the problems associated with the formation of selenium and organoselenides, which commonly arise in oxidations using molar quantities of selenium dioxide, are not encountered.

1. Department of Chemistry, University of Canterbury, Christchurch, New Zealand.
2. M. P. Hartshorn and A. F. A. Wallis, J. Chem. Soc. London, 5254 (1964).
3. G. O. Schenck, H. Eggert, and W. Denk, Justus Liebigs Ann. Chem., 584, 177 (1953).
4. J. M. Quinn, J. Chem. Eng. Data, 9, 389 (1964).
5. J. K. Crandall and L. C. Crawley, Org. Syn., 53, 17 (1973) and references cited therein.

CARBOXYLATION OF AROMATIC COMPOUNDS: FERROCENECARBOXYLIC ACID

[Ferrocene, carboxy-]

Submitted by Perry C. Reeves[1]
Checked by J. J. Mrowca, M. M. Borecki,
and William A. Sheppard

1. Procedure

A. *(2-Chlorobenzoyl)ferrocene* [*Ferrocene, (2-chlorobenzoyl)-*]. A thoroughly dried, 1-l., three-necked, round-bottomed flask is equipped with a mechanical stirrer, a funnel for the addition of air-sensitive solids (Note 1), and a two-necked adapter holding a thermometer and a gas-inlet tube. Throughout the ensuing reaction a positive pressure of dry nitrogen is applied to the system through the gas inlet. The flask is charged with 18.6 g. (0.10 mole) of ferrocene (Note 2), 17.5 g. (0.10 mole) of 2-chlorobenzoyl chloride [Benzoyl chloride, 2-chloro-] (Note 3), and 200 ml. of dichloromethane, and the addition funnel is charged with 14.0 g. (0.10 mole) of anhydrous aluminum chloride. Stirring is begun, and the flask is immersed in an ice bath. When the solution has been chilled thoroughly, the aluminum chloride is added in small portions at such a rate that the reaction mixture remains below 5°. The appearance of a deep blue color indicates that the reaction is occurring. This addition requires about 20 minutes, and after its completion stirring is continued for 30 minutes with ice cooling and for 2 hours at room temperature.

The reaction mixture is cooled again in ice, 200 ml. of water is added cautiously, and the resultant two-phase mixture is stirred vigorously

28

for 30 minutes. After transferring the mixture to a separatory funnel, the layers are separated, and the aqueous layer is extracted with two 50-ml. portions of dichloromethane. The combined dichloromethane solutions are washed once with 50 ml. of water, twice with 50-ml. portions of 10% aqueous sodium hydroxide, and finally dried over magnesium sulfate. Filtration and evaporation to dryness at reduced pressure yields a viscous, red liquid, which gradually solidifies to a dark red solid. The yield of crude (2-chlorobenzoyl)ferrocene is 30.4–30.9 g. (94–96%) (Note 4).

B. *Ferrocenecarboxylic Acid.* A dry, 500-ml., three-necked, round-bottomed flask is equipped with a mechanical stirrer and a reflux condenser topped with a nitrogen-inlet tube and then charged with 250 ml. of 1,2-dimethoxyethane (Note 5) and 46.0 g. (0.41 mole) of potassium *tert*-butoxide [2-Propanol, 2-methyl-, potassium salt] (Note 6). A nitrogen atmosphere is established in the system, and 2.2 ml. (0.12 mole) of water (Note 6) is added with stirring, producing a slurry. The crude (2-chlorobenzoyl)ferrocene prepared in Part A is then added, giving a red solution, which is stirred and refluxed under nitrogen. As the reaction proceeds the color fades to tan, and after 1 hour at reflux the reaction mixture is cooled and poured into 1 l. of water. The resulting solution is washed with three 150-ml. portions of ether, which are combined and back-extracted with two 50-ml. portions of 10% aqueous sodium hydroxide. The aqueous phases are then combined and acidified with concentrated hydrochloric acid. The precipitate is collected by filtration and air dried to give 17.0–19.2 g. (74–83% from ferrocene) of ferrocenecarboxylic acid as an air-stable yellow powder, m.p. 214–216° (decomp.) (Note 7).

2. Notes

1. If such a funnel is not available, an Erlenmeyer flask connected to the reaction flask by a length of thin-walled rubber tubing (Gooch tubing) may be substituted. In this case, the reaction mixture must not be stirred so vigorously that liquid is splashed up into the neck of the flask, which would cause aluminum chloride to cake there and prevent it from falling into the flask.

2. Ferrocene was purchased from Strem Chemicals Incorporated, Danvers, Massachusetts.

3. 2-Chlorobenzoyl chloride was purchased from Aldrich Chemical Company, Inc. and used as received with a stated purity of 95%.

4. The crude material contains approximately 5% of unreacted ferrocene. Recrystallization from heptane affords pure (2-chlorobenzoyl)-ferrocene as scarlet needles, m.p. 99–100°; however, the crude material may be used without purification for Part B.

5. 1,2-Dimethoxyethane was distilled from calcium hydride immediately prior to use.

6. Potassium *tert*-butoxide was purchased from Columbia Organic Chemicals Company, Columbia, South Carolina. The molar ratio of potassium *tert*-butoxide to water is critical, and the amounts specified represent optimum quantities for cleavage of 0.10 mole of ketone.[2,3]

7. The decomposition point is obtained in a sealed capillary tube and is not corrected. As the solid is heated, it first changes from yellow to brownish red and then decomposes to a dark red liquid. The decomposition temperature of this compound has been reported to be 208.5°,[4] 224–225°,[5] and 225–230°.[6]

The crude product is suitable for most purposes. It may be recrystallized from toluene (1 g. in 15–20 ml. of solvent, 80% recovery in the first crop) to give material melting at 220–222° (decomp.).

3. Discussion

The carboxylic acids of organometallic systems are important synthetic intermediates that have been prepared by many different synthetic methods. Ferrocenecarboxylic acid has been studied the most extensively,[7] and the best laboratory syntheses previously reported involve hydrolysis of cyanoferrocene [Ferrocene, cyano-][8] or of *S*-methylferrocenethiocarbonate [Ferrocene, [(methylthio)thioxo-methyl]-].[9]

The present synthesis[10] consists of two simple steps, uses readily available and inexpensive starting materials, and produces pure material in high overall yield. It is based on two observations: that nonenolizable ketones may be cleaved to carboxylic acids by potassium *tert*-butoxide–water,[2] and that aryl 2-chlorophenyl ketones may be cleaved with loss of the 2-chlorophenyl group to give only one of the two possible acids.[11] Other compounds prepared by this route include carboxycyclopentadienyltricarbonylmanganese [Manganese, tricarbonyl[(1,2,3,4,5-η)-1-carboxy-2,4-cyclopentadien-1-yl]-] (79%)[10] and several substituted benzoic acids:[11] biphenyl-4-carboxylic acid [[1,1'-Biphenyl]-4-carboxylic acid] (64%), 3,4-dimethylbenzoic acid [Benzoic acid, 3,4-dimethyl-] (57%), 2,4,6-trimethylbenzoic acid [Benzoic acid, 2,4,6-trimethyl-] (59%), 3,4-dimethoxybenzoic acid [Benzoic acid, 3,4-dimethoxy-] (73%), and 2,4-dimethoxybenzoic acid [Benzoic acid, 2,4-dimethoxy-] (60%). In cases where the cleavage reaction proceeds in low yield, substitution of 2,6-dichlorobenzoyl chloride [Benzoyl chloride, 2,6-dichloro-] for 2-chlorobenzoyl chloride may be helpful. With thiophene, for example, the yield of carboxylic acid was increased from 10% to 72% by this modification.[11]

1. Department of Chemistry, Southern Methodist University, Dallas, Texas 75275. This work was supported by the Robert A. Welch Foundation.
2. G. A. Swan, *J. Chem. Soc. London*, 1408 (1948).
3. P. G. Gassman, J. T. Lumb, and F. V. Zalar, *J. Amer. Chem. Soc.*, **89**, 946 (1967).
4. K. L. Rinehart, K. L. Motz, and S. Moon, *J. Amer. Chem. Soc.*, **79**, 2749 (1957).
5. R. L. Schaaf, *J. Org. Chem.*, **27**, 107 (1962).
6. V. Weinmayr, *J. Amer. Chem. Soc.*, **77**, 3009 (1955).
7. D. E. Bublitz and K. L. Rinehart, *Org. React.*, **17**, 1 (1969).
8. A. N. Nesmeyanov, E. G. Perevalova, and L. P. Jaryeva, *Chem. Ber.*, **93**, 2729 (1960).
9. D. E. Bublitz and G. H. Harris, *J. Organometal. Chem.*, **4**, 404 (1965).
10. E. R. Biehl and P. C. Reeves, *Synthesis*, 360 (1973).
11. M. Derenberg and P. Hodge, *Tetrahedron Lett.*, 3825 (1971).

CHAIN ELONGATION OF ALKENES
via gem-DIHALOCYCLOPROPANES:
1,1-DIPHENYL-2-BROMO-3-ACETOXY-1-PROPENE

[2-Propen-1-ol, 2-bromo-3,3-diphenyl-, acetate]

Submitted by STANLEY R. SANDLER[1]
Checked by D. W. BROOKS and S. MASAMUNE

1. Procedure

A. 1,1-*Dibromo*-2,2-*diphenylcyclopropane* [*Benzene, 1,1'-(2,2-dibromo-cyclopropylidene)bis*-]. A 500-ml., three-necked, round-bottomed flask is equipped with a mechanical stirrer, a dropping funnel, and a condenser fitted with a drying tube. The flask is flushed with dry nitrogen and then charged with 25.0 g. (0.14 mole) of 1,1-diphenylethylene [Benzene, 1,1'-ethenylidenebis-] (Note 1), 100 ml. of pentane, and 28 g. (0.25 mole) of potassium *tert*-butoxide [2-Propanol, 2-methyl-, potassium salt] (Note 2). The mixture is stirred and cooled to 0°, and 66.0 g. (0.26 mole) of bromoform [Methane, tribromo-] (Note 3) is added dropwise during 30–45 minutes. Stirring is continued for an additional 2–3 hours at room temperature, and then 200 ml. of water is added. The yellowish insoluble product is filtered, dried, and digested with 300 ml. of refluxing 2-propanol for 30 minutes. After cooling, the product is filtered and washed with 100 ml. of 2-propanol to provide 31–38 g. (63–78%) of colorless crystals, m.p. 151–152°.

B. 1,1-*Diphenyl-2-bromo-3-acetoxy*-1-*propene.*   A 250-ml. flask equipped with a condenser is charged with 17.6 g. (0.050 mole) of 1,1-dibromo-2,2-diphenylcyclopropane, 12.5 g. (0.075 mole) of silver acetate [Acetic acid, silver(1 +) salt] (Note 4), and 50 ml. of glacial acetic acid, then immersed in an oil bath at 100–120° for 24 hours (Note 5). After cooling, the mixture is diluted with 200 ml. of ether and filtered. The ethereal filtrate is washed with two 100-ml. portions of water, two 100-ml. portions of aqueous saturated sodium carbonate, and finally with two 100-ml. portions of water. After drying over anhydrous sodium sulfate, the ether is removed on a rotary evaporator. Distillation of the resulting residue under reduced pressure yields 12.0 g. (72%) of the product, b.p. 142–145° (0.15 mm.), n_D^{22} 1.6020–1.6023 (Note 6).

2. Notes

1. 1,1-Diphenylethylene was purchased from Eastman Organic Chemicals.

2. Potassium *tert*-butoxide was supplied by Mine Safety Appliances (MSA) Research Corporation.

3. Bromoform was supplied by the Dow Chemical Company and used without further purification.

4. The silver acetate can be replaced by a mixture of sodium acetate and silver nitrate.

5. A 24-hour period may not be required but was found to be a convenient choice in this case.

6. Ultraviolet (methanol) nm. max. (log ϵ): 260 (3.94); proton magnetic resonance (CDCl$_3$) δ, number of protons, multiplicity: 2.08 (3, singlet), 4.87 (2, singlet), 7.3 (10, multiplet).

3. Discussion

The present procedure is that of the submitter[2] and illustrates a general method for the chain extension of alkenes *via gem*-dihalocyclopropanes earlier described by Skell and Sandler.[3] The reaction of dihalocyclopropanes with electrophilic reagents yields a haloallylic derivative,[2] the thermal reaction yields haloallylic halides or halodienes, and the reaction with magnesium, sodium, or lithium alkyl reagents yields allenes.[2] These reactions are summarized in the formula that follows, and some examples are given in Table I.

This general method has been used by Parham and coworkers[4] to transform indenes into β-halonaphthalenes. Other references in the literature indicate that this method is also useful for the conversion of pyrroles to β-substituted pyridines and of indoles to β-haloquinolines.[3]

TABLE I

Chain Elongation of Alkenes *via* gem-Dibromocyclopropanes

Alkene	Conditions for Dibromocyclopropane Opening	Product
	$AgNO_3$, H_2O	
	Heat	
	CH_3CO_2Ag, CH_3CO_2H	

TABLE I (*continued*)

Alkene	Conditions for Dibromocyclopropane Opening	Product
C_6H_5 ⌿	CH_3CO_2Ag, CH_3CO_2H	C_6H_5 ⌿ Br ⌿ O_2CCH_3
⌿ (Z) or (E)	CH_3CO_2Ag, CH_3CO_2H	Br ⌿ O_2CCH_3
⌿	Heat or CH_3CO_2Ag, CH_3CO_2H	Br ⌿
⌿	CH_3CO_2Ag, CH_3CO_2H	Br ⌿ O_2CCH_3 + Br ⌿
⌿	CH_3CO_2Ag, CH_3CO_2H	Br ⌿ O_2CCH_3 + Br ⌿ CH_3CO_2

1. Borden, Inc., Chemical Division, Central Research Laboratory, Philadelphia, Pennsylvania 19124. Present address: Pennwalt Corp., King of Prussia, Pennsylvania 19406.
2. S. R. Sandler, *J. Org. Chem.*, **32**, 3876 (1967) and references cited therein.
3. P. S. Skell and S. R. Sandler, *J. Amer. Chem. Soc.*, **80**, 2024 (1958).
4. W. E. Parham and H. E. Reiff, *J. Amer. Chem. Soc.*, **77**, 1177 (1955) and subsequent papers on the reaction of indenes with dihalocarbenes to yield β-halonaphthalenes.

CONVERSION OF NITRO TO CARBONYL
BY OZONOLYSIS OF NITRONATES:
2,5-HEPTANEDIONE

Submitted by JOHN E. MCMURRY and JACK MELTON[1]
Checked by ROBERT M. COATES and ROBERT W. MASON

1. Procedure

A. *5-Nitroheptan-2-one* [*2-Heptanone, 5-nitro-*]. A 500-ml., three-necked flask equipped with a magnetic stirring bar, a 50-ml. addition funnel, and a condenser fitted with a nitrogen-inlet tube is flushed with nitrogen and charged with 35.7 ml. (36.0 g., 0.40 mole) of 1-nitropropane [Propane, 1-nitro-], 20.0 ml. (14.4 g., 0.14 mole) of diisopropylamine [*N*-(1-Methylethyl)-2-propanamine] (Note 1), and 200 ml. of chloroform. The resulting solution is stirred and heated to 60°, and 28 g. (0.40 mole) of methyl vinyl ketone [3-Buten-2-one] is added dropwise over a 2-hour period. The reaction mixture is then stirred for another 16 hours at 60°, allowed to cool to room temperature, and transferred to a 500-ml. separatory funnel, where it is washed with two 30-ml. portions of water and 30 ml. of 5% aqueous hydrochloric acid. After drying over anhydrous sodium sulfate, the chloroform solution is concentrated with a rotary evaporator. Distillation of the residue under reduced pressure gives 39.1 g. (61%) of 5-nitroheptan-2-one, b.p. 65–70° (0.2 mm.), n_D^{20} 1.4403 (Note 2).

B. *2,5-Heptanedione*. Methanolic sodium methoxide [Methanol, sodium salt] is prepared by cautiously adding small pieces of freshly cut sodium (5.67 g., 0.247 mole) to 200 ml. of cold methanol (Note 3) in a 500-ml., three-necked flask equipped with a mechanical stirrer, a

50-ml. addition funnel, and a condenser fitted with a nitrogen-inlet tube. The resulting solution is stirred and cooled in an ice bath while 38.6 g. (0.243 mole) of 5-nitroheptan-2-one is added over 15 minutes, after which stirring is continued for another 15 minutes at 0°. The ice bath is then replaced by an acetone–dry ice bath, the nitrogen-inlet tube and addition funnel are removed, and a fritted-glass dispersion tube is inserted into the solution. With continued cooling and vigorous stirring, an ozone–oxygen mixture is bubbled through the solution for 5 hours (Notes 4 and 5).

After ozone generation has been stopped, pure oxygen is passed through the reaction mixture to remove excess ozone. Dry ice cooling is continued while 21 g. (0.34 mole) of dimethyl sulfide [Methane, thiobis-] is added in one portion (Note 6), and the mixture is then allowed to come to ambient temperature overnight (18 hours). Methanol is removed with a rotary evaporator, and the residual liquid is dissolved in 250 ml. of ether. This solution is allowed to percolate through a short mat of silica gel (50 g.) to remove polar impurities and is then concentrated with a rotary evaporator, leaving a residue which is stirred with 30 ml. of 5% aqueous hydrochloric acid for 45 minutes (Note 7). Chloroform (40 ml.) is added, the organic layer is separated, and the aqueous phase is further extracted with two 30-ml. portions of chloroform. The organic extracts are combined, washed with saturated aqueous sodium bicarbonate, dried over anhydrous sodium sulfate, filtered, and concentrated with a rotary evaporator. Vacuum distillation of the residue with a Kugelrohr apparatus gives 22.7 g. (73%) of 2,5-heptanedione, b.p. 90° (20 mm.), n_D^{20} 1.4313 (Note 8).

2. Notes

1. Nitropropane from MC and B Manufacturing Chemists and methyl vinyl ketone and diisopropylamine from Aldrich Chemical Company, Inc. were used as supplied.

2. Infrared (neat) cm.$^{-1}$: 1715, 1545; proton magnetic resonance (CCl$_4$) δ, number of protons, multiplicity, coupling constant J in Hz.: 0.97 (3, triplet, $J = 7$), 2.13 (3, singlet), 4.38 (1, multiplet).

3. By using 300 ml. of methanol at this point, the checkers were able to avoid crust formation on the gas-dispersion tube during ozonolysis (see Note 5).

4. Ozone was generated using a Welsbach ozonator at a total gas flow

of 1.0 l. per minute at 115 volts. This corresponds to an ozone flow of 0.104 mole per hour, and thus the time theoretically required to generate one equivalent of ozone in this reaction is 2.3 hours. The use of excess ozone is permissible only for secondary nitronates (see Discussion).

5. The precipitate that forms during ozonolysis sometimes impedes stirring, and in some cases it may be necessary to dilute the slurry with another 100 ml. of methanol after the first hour. Solid can also clog the gas-dispersion tube. The submitters scraped the fritted-glass tip occasionally to maintain a constant flow rate, whereas the checkers prepared a more dilute solution of nitronate anion (Note 3).

6. Dimethyl sulfide is added as a safety precaution. It reduces any highly oxidized and potentially dangerous by-products that might have formed during ozonolysis.

7. Acid treatment hydrolyzes dimethyl ketal by-products, which form to the extent of 5–10% during the reaction.

8. Infrared (neat) cm.$^{-1}$: 1710; proton magnetic resonance (CCl$_4$) δ, number of protons, multiplicity, coupling constant J in Hz.: 1.01 (3, triplet, $J = 7$), 2.11 (3, singlet), 2.58 (4, singlet), 2.41 (2, quartet, $J = 7$). Gas chromatographic analysis by the checkers (6.3 mm. by 3 m. column of 20% SE-30 on Chromosorb W, 185°, 60 ml. of helium per minute) showed the presence of two minor impurities with retention times of 1.0 and 2.7 minutes. The major product, 2,5-heptanedione, had a retention time of 2.4 minutes.

3. Discussion

There are various methods available for transforming a nitro group into a carbonyl group, including the Nef reaction (strongly acidic),[2] permanganate oxidation of nitronate anions (basic, oxidative),[3] persulfate oxidation of nitronates (basic, oxidative),[4] treatment with a mixture of organic and inorganic nitrite (neutral, oxidative),[5] and treatment of either a free nitro compound or a nitronate anion with aqueous titanous ion (neutral, reductive).[6] Each method is limited, however, by poor yield, inconvenience, or lack of generality.

With the proviso that the substrate not contain a reactive carbon-carbon double bond, the present ozonolysis procedure[7] appears to provide a convenient and efficient method for carrying out the desired transformation. As can be seen in Table I, both primary and secondary nitronates undergo the reaction. If a primary nitronate is to be used, however, one equivalent of ozone must be slowly metered in since use of an excess leads to overoxidation.

TABLE I

R_2CHNO_2 $\xrightarrow{CH_3O^-}$ $\xrightarrow{O_3}$ $R_2C{=}O$		Yield (%)
		73
		68
		65
		88

1. Thimann Laboratories, University of California, Santa Cruz, California 95064.
2. W. E. Noland, *Chem. Rev.*, **55**, 137 (1955).
3. H. Shechter and F. T. Williams, *J. Org. Chem.*, **27**, 3699 (1962).
4. A. H. Pagano and H. Shechter, *J. Org. Chem.*, **35**, 295 (1970).
5. N. Kornblum and P. A. Wade, *J. Org. Chem.*, **38**, 1418 (1973).
6. J. E. McMurry and J. Melton, *J. Org. Chem.*, **38**, 4367 (1973).
7. J. E. McMurry, J. Melton, and H. Padgett, *J. Org. Chem.*, **39**, 259 (1974). We have recently been informed that ozonolysis of nitronate anions was first reported in a paper by F. Asinger, *Ber.*, **77**, 73 (1944).

CONVERSION OF PRIMARY ALCOHOLS TO URETHANES
via THE INNER SALT OF METHYL
(CARBOXYSULFAMOYL)TRIETHYLAMMONIUM HYDROXIDE:
METHYL *n*-HEXYLCARBAMATE

[Carbamic acid, hexyl-, methyl ester]

Submitted by Edward M. Burgess, Harold R. Penton, Jr.,
E. Alan Taylor, and W. Michael Williams[1]
Checked by James E. Nottke and Richard E. Benson

1. Procedure

Caution! Chlorosulfonyl isocyanate is highly corrosive. This preparation should be carried out in an efficient hood, and rubber gloves should be worn during the first step.

A. *Methyl (Chlorosulfonyl)carbamate* [*Carbamic acid, (chlorosulfonyl)-, methyl ester*]. A dry, two-necked, 500-ml., round-bottomed flask is

40

fitted with a magnetic stirring bar, a 125-ml., pressure-equalizing dropping funnel, and a reflux condenser to which is attached a calcium chloride drying tube. The flask is charged with a solution of 70.8 g. (43.6 ml., 0.50 mole) of chlorosulfonyl isocyanate [Sulfuryl chloride isocyanate] (Note 1) in 150 ml. of anhydrous benzene (Note 2), and a solution of 16.0 g. (20.2 ml., 0.50 mole) of anhydrous methanol (Note 3) in 25 ml. of anhydrous benzene (Note 2) is placed in the dropping funnel. The flask is immersed in a water bath (Note 4), stirring is begun, and the methanol–benzene solution is added dropwise during 0.5 hour. Cold water is added to the bath as required to maintain a temperature of 25–30°. The reaction mixture is stirred for an additional 0.5 hour, and then 125 ml. of olefin-free hexane (Note 5) is added from the addition funnel over a 5-minute period while cooling the flask to 0–5° with an ice bath. The moisture-sensitive product is removed by filtration, washed twice with 40 ml. of hexane, and dried under reduced pressure to give 76–80 g. (88–92%) of methyl (chlorosulfonyl)carbamate as white crystals, m.p. 72–74° (Note 6). This material should be stored in a brown bottle protected from light (Note 7).

B. *Inner Salt of Methyl (Carboxysulfamoyl)triethylammonium Hydroxide* [*Ethanaminium, N,N-diethyl-N-[[(methoxycarbonyl)amino]sulfonyl]-, hydroxide, inner salt*]. A two-necked, 500-ml., round-bottomed flask is fitted with a magnetic stirring bar, a 500-ml., pressure-equalizing dropping funnel, and a condenser to which a calcium chloride drying tube is attached. A solution of 23.0 g. (31.8 ml., 0.225 mole) of anhydrous triethylamine [Ethanamine, *N,N*-diethyl-] (Note 8) in 50 ml. of anhydrous benzene (Note 2) is placed in the flask, stirring is begun, and a solution of 17.4 g. (0.100 mole) of methyl (chlorosulfonyl)carbamate in 225 ml. of dried benzene (Note 9) is added dropwise during 1 hour. During addition the flask is cooled with a water bath maintained at 10–15°. The resulting mixture is stirred at 25–30° for an additional 0.5 hour and then filtered to remove triethylamine hydrochloride (13.8 g.). Evaporation of the filtrate under reduced pressure leaves 22–23 g. of light tan needles, m.p. 70–72° (decomp.), which is dissolved in 160 ml. of anhydrous tetrahydrofuran (Note 10) at 30°. On cooling, 20.0–20.6 g. (84–86%) of the inner salt of methyl (carboxysulfamoyl)-triethylammonium hydroxide precipitates as colorless needles, m.p. 70–72° (decomp.) (Note 11).

C. *Methyl n-Hexylcarbamate*. In a dry, 100-ml., round-bottomed flask fitted with a reflux condenser, to which a calcium chloride drying tube is attached, are placed a boiling chip, 14.8 g. (0.062 mole) of the inner salt of methyl (carboxysulfamoyl)triethylammonium hydroxide, and 6.0 g. (0.058 mole) of freshly distilled 1-hexanol (Note 12). After a mildly exothermic reaction (occasionally there is a 5-minute induction period), the viscous yellow reaction mixture is heated with an oil bath at 95° for 1 hour. The mixture is then cooled to 30°, diluted with 50 ml. of water, and extracted with three 50-ml. portions of dichloromethane. The organic extracts are combined, washed successively with 100 ml. of 5% aqueous hydrochloric acid and 50 ml. of water, and dried over anhydrous magnesium sulfate. After filtration to remove the drying agent, dichloromethane is removed under reduced pressure using a rotary evaporator. The residue is triturated with 50 ml. of anhydrous ether and filtered, and the recovered solid is triturated with two further 50-ml. portions of ether. The three ethereal filtrates are combined and concentrated with a rotary evaporator to afford 8.0 g. of crude product. Fractionation of this oil through a short-path distillation apparatus gives 4.8–4.9 g. (51–52%) of methyl n-hexylcarbamate as a colorless oil, b.p. 59–60° (0.08 mm.); n_D^{20} 1.4361 (Note 13).

2. Notes

1. The preparation of chlorosulfonyl isocyanate is described in *Org. Syn.*, Coll. Vol. **5**, 226 (1973). This compound is highly corrosive, reacts explosively with water, and may be contaminated with cyanogen chloride.

2. Throughout this preparation the submitters used reagent-grade materials distilled prior to use. The checkers used ACS reagent-grade benzene available from Fisher Scientific Company.

3. The checkers used ACS reagent-grade methanol available from Fisher Scientific Company.

4. The water bath should not be positioned around the flask until after the solution of chlorosulfonyl isocyanate has been added.

5. The checkers used spectro-grade reagent available from Phillips Petroleum Company.

6. Proton magnetic resonance (CD_3CN) δ: 3.64 (singlet).

7. The checkers observed a violent decomposition when product stored in a clear glass container was inadvertently exposed to sunlight.

8. Triethylamine was dried by distillation from phosphorus pentoxide at atmospheric pressure. The checkers used reagent-grade material available from Eastman Organic Chemicals.

9. The compound dissolves readily in benzene on warming to 40°.

10. The checkers used ACS reagent-grade material available from Fisher Scientific Company, taken from a freshly opened bottle.

11. Infrared $(CHCl_3)$ cm.$^{-1}$: 1690 (C=O), 1345, 1110 (SO_2), 1260 (C—O); proton magnetic resonance $(CDCl_3)$ δ, number of protons, multiplicity, coupling constant J in Hz.: 1.15 (9, triplet, $J = 7$), 3.29 (6, quartet, $J = 7$), 3.66 (3, singlet).

12. The checkers used practical-grade material (available from Eastman Organic Chemicals), which they distilled immediately prior to use.

13. Infrared (neat) cm.$^{-1}$: 3400, 2950, 1700, 1520, 1255, 1190, 774; proton magnetic resonance (neat) δ, number of protons, multiplicity: 0.8–1.5 (13, multiplet), 3.6 (3, singlet), 6.14 (1, broad triplet).

3. Discussion

The above procedure describes the only known preparation of the inner salt of methyl (carboxysulfamoyl)triethylammonium hydroxide and illustrates the use of this reagent to convert a primary alcohol to the corresponding urethane.[2] Hydrolysis of the urethane would then provide the primary amine. The method is limited to primary alcohols; secondary and tertiary alcohols are dehydrated to olefins under these conditions, often in synthetically useful yields.[2]

Other sequences that transform primary alcohols to primary amines include: (a) conversion of the alcohol to a cyanate, rearrangement to an isocyanate, and hydrolysis,[3] and (b) conversion of the alcohol to an N-alkylformamide via the Ritter reaction, followed by hydrolysis.[4]

1. School of Chemistry, Georgia Institute of Technology, Atlanta, Georgia 30332. This work was supported by a grant (GM-12672) from the National Institutes of Health.
2. E. M. Burgess, H. R. Penton, Jr., and E. A. Taylor, *J. Org. Chem.*, **38**, 26 (1973).
3. J. W. Timberlake and J. C. Martin, *J. Org. Chem.*, **33**, 4054 (1968).
4. L. I. Krimen and D. J. Cota, *Org. React.*, **17**, 213 (1969).

DEMETHYLATION OF METHYL ARYL ETHERS: 4-ETHOXY-3-HYDROXYBENZALDEHYDE

[Benzaldehyde, 4-ethoxy-3-hydroxy-]

Submitted by ROBERT E. IRELAND and DAVID M. WALBA[1]
Checked by R. ANDERSEN and G. BÜCHI

1. Procedure

A. *4-Ethoxy-3-methoxybenzaldehyde Ethylene Acetal* [*1,3-Dioxolane, 2-(4-ethoxy-3-methoxyphenyl)*-]. A 500-ml., three-necked flask with vertical necks is fitted with a magnetic stirring bar and a water separator of about 30-ml. capacity, to which is attached a condenser topped with an argon inlet. The flask is charged with 300 mg. (0.00158 mole) of *p*-toluenesulfonic acid monohydrate [Benzenesulfonic acid, 4-methyl-, monohydrate], 270 ml. of benzene (Note 1), 30 ml. (0.535 mole) of ethylene glycol [1,2-Ethanediol], and 5.0 g. (0.0277 mole) of 4-ethoxy-3-methoxybenzaldehyde [Benzaldehyde, 4-ethoxy-3-methoxy-] (Note

44

2) and then placed under a positive pressure of argon, which is maintained throughout the reaction. Vigorous stirring is begun, and the solution is brought to reflux by means of an oil bath at about 110°.

After 20 hours at reflux, the mixture is cooled to room temperature using a water bath and then poured with vigorous stirring into 500 ml. of 10% aqueous potassium carbonate contained in a 1-l. separatory funnel. The benzene layer is washed with two 250-ml. portions of 10% aqueous potassium carbonate and 250 ml. of brine containing potassium carbonate (Note 3), dried over sodium sulfate for about 10 minutes, and filtered. Removal of the solvent on a rotary evaporator with the water bath at 25–35° provides a solid yellow residue, which is dried under vacuum.

To obtain a crystalline product, a solution of the residue in 30 ml. of benzene containing a few drops of triethylamine (Note 4) is placed in a 250-ml. Erlenmeyer flask, heated gently on a steam bath, and diluted with 150 ml. of hexane. Heating is continued for about 5 minutes (Note 5), after which the solution is allowed to cool to room temperature, seeded, and put in a freezer at −15° for at least 5 hours. The resulting solid is collected by suction filtration and washed with cold hexane. After vacuum drying, 5.8 g. (94%) of light cream-colored crystals, m.p. 75–77°, is obtained.

B. *4-Ethoxy-3-hydroxybenzaldehyde.* A 100-ml., three-necked flask containing a magnetic stirring bar and fitted with an argon inlet, a rubber septum, and a ground-glass stopper in the center neck is evacuated and flame-dried. The flask is allowed to cool under a positive pressure of argon, which is maintained throughout the following sequence. Using a syringe, 30 ml. of dry tetrahydrofuran (Note 6) and 5.0 ml. (0.0289 mole) of diphenylphosphine [Phosphine, diphenyl-] (Note 7) are added through the septum. The resulting solution is stirred and cooled with an ice bath, and 15 ml. (0.0318 mole) of cold 2.12 M n-butyllithium–hexane solution [Lithium, butyl] (Note 8) is added by syringe during *ca.* 3 minutes. Stirring is continued as the red solution is allowed to warm to room temperature over about 30 minutes, and then 5.0 g. (0.0222 mole) of 4-ethoxy-3-methoxybenzaldehyde ethylene acetal is added through the center neck. The flask is stoppered, and the mixture is stirred at room temperature for 2 hours.

The reaction mixture is then poured into a 500-ml. Erlenmeyer flask containing 200 ml. of vigorously stirred water, 10 ml. of 10% aqueous sodium hydroxide is added, and the mixture is transferred to a 500-ml.

separatory funnel. The reaction vessel and Erlenmeyer flask are rinsed with water, and the rinsings are also poured into the funnel. Alkali-insoluble impurities are removed by washing the basic aqueous phase with four 100-ml. portions of ether, which are combined and back-extracted with two 50-ml. portions of 10% aqueous sodium hydroxide. The combined aqueous layers are then put into a 1-l. Erlenmeyer flask, cooled in an ice bath, and acidified with concentrated hydrochloric acid to a Congo red end point. During acidification the clear yellow basic solution becomes cloudy white. This milky suspension is stirred without cooling for 3 minutes and then extracted with 200 ml. of ether and two 100-ml. portions of ether. The combined ether layers are washed successively with 100 ml. of water and 100 ml. of saturated aqueous sodium chloride, dried over magnesium sulfate, and filtered. Removal of solvent with a rotary evaporator provides a residue that is vacuum dried to give 3.58–3.60 g. (97–98%) of a slightly yellow solid, m.p. 121.5–126°. One recrystallization from 20 ml. of benzene gives almost white crystals which are vacuum dried to afford 3.21–3.29 g. (87–88%) of 4-hydroxy-3-ethoxybenzaldehyde, m.p. 125.5–127° (Notes 9 and 10).

2. Notes

1. Reagent-grade benzene was used without further purification.

2. Practical-grade 4-ethoxy-3-methoxybenzaldehyde (4-ethoxy-*m*-anisaldehyde) was obtained by the submitters from MC and B Manufacturing Chemists and by the checkers from Aldrich Chemical Company, Inc. This material was purified by distillation (b.p. 125–135°/0.1 mm.), followed by one recrystallization from cyclohexane (100 ml./10 g. crude solid). Colorless crystals, m.p. 60–62°, were obtained after filtration and vacuum drying. Purification of 20 g. of the commercial material gave about 15 g. of recrystallized product.

3. This solution is prepared by dilution of 25 ml. of 10% aqueous potassium carbonate to 250 ml. with saturated aqueous sodium chloride.

4. Triethylamine was distilled from calcium hydride prior to use. It is added to the benzene to protect the sensitive acetal from hydrolysis.

5. It is not necessary to boil the solution. This heating merely serves to prevent crystals from coming out of solution too fast on addition of the hexane.

6. Tetrahydrofuran was purified and dried according to the procedure described in *Org. Syn.*, **46**, 105 (1966).

7. Commercial diphenylphosphine obtained from Orgmet, Inc. may be used without further purification. Alternatively, the material may be prepared from triphenylphosphine as follows. A 2-l., three-necked flask containing a magnetic stirring bar and fitted with an argon inlet is charged with 120 g. (0.46 mole) of triphenylphosphine [Phosphine, triphenyl] and 1 l. of dry tetrahydrofuran (Note 6). To the stirred solution is added 18.42 g. (2.66 moles, 542 cm. of 1/8-inch diameter wire) of lithium wire, which has been washed with hexane and dried carefully with a paper towel. (*Caution! If the towel is rubbed against the lithium too fast, a fire will result.*) Lithium is added by cutting 3–5-mm. segments directly into the center neck of the flask with scissors. A slow argon flow is maintained throughout the addition, which requires about 20 minutes. The flask is stoppered, and the red solution is stirred for 2.5 hours under argon.

The solution is then filtered through a piece of glass wool (fitted loosely in a funnel) into a 2-l. beaker containing 600 g. of crushed ice. A glass rod is used to stir the mixture, and the reaction vessel and filter are rinsed with ether. There result two clear phases, which are transferred to a 2-l. separatory funnel and extracted with four 200-ml. portions of ether. The combined ether layers are washed with 250 ml. of aqueous 5% hydrochloric acid, 250 ml. of water, and two 250-ml. portions of saturated aqueous sodium chloride and then dried over magnesium sulfate for about $\frac{1}{2}$ hour. Since diphenylphosphine is unstable toward air oxidation, especially in dilute ether solution, the extractions should be carried out as quickly as possible. After gravity filtration to remove the drying agent, the ether solution is stripped on a rotary evaporator, and the residue is vacuum dried to yield 83.7 g. (99%) of crude product. Pure material is then obtained by distillation. The submitters used a small (14/20 joints, 15 cm. long) Vigreux column and observed b.p. 90–103° (0.06 mm.). Using a 20-cm. Vigreux column, the checkers observed b.p. 95–115° (0.06 mm.). In either case, the yield of clear liquid was 62 g. (74%). If the product is stored under argon in a bottle sealed with a rubber serum cap, it is stable for months at room temperature. *Caution! Care should be taken not to get any diphenylphosphine on a paper towel, as it may ignite spontaneously.*

8. *n*-Butyllithium in hexane was obtained from Ventron Corporation and stored in a refrigerator under argon. The solution was titrated with 2-butanol in xylene, using 1,10-phenanthroline as indicator.

9. The literature m.p. for colorless crystals is 127–128°.[2]

10. Infrared (CHCl$_3$) cm.$^{-1}$: 3550 (OH), 1680 (C=O), 1610, 1580, 1510, 1470; proton magnetic resonance (CDCl$_3$) δ, number of protons, multiplicity, coupling constant J in Hz.: 9.80 (1, singlet, ArCHO), 7.4 (2, multiplet, aryl CH), 6.90 (1, doublet, J = 10, aryl CH), 5.44 (1, broad, OH), 4.19 (2, quartet, J = 7, —CH_2CH$_3$), 1.47 (3, triplet, J = 7, —CH$_2$CH_3).

3. Discussion

4-Ethoxy-3-hydroxybenzaldehyde (isobourbonal) has been prepared in good yield (84%) by ethylation of 3,4-dihydroxybenzaldehyde [Benzaldehyde, 3,4-dihydroxy-] with diethyl sulfate [Sulfuric acid, diethyl ester] in dimethylformamide.[2]

The present procedure illustrates the facile demethylation of methyl aryl ethers by lithium diphenylphosphide.[3] This reaction is specific for methyl ethers and may be carried out in the presence of ethyl ethers in high yield.[4] Use of excess reagent allows cleavage in the presence of enolizable ketones.[5] In the present case, the cleavage may be performed without protection of the aldehyde, but two equivalents of reagent are required, and the yield is reduced to ca. 60%.

The exact time and temperature required for complete reaction must be determined for each individual compound. It has been observed that nucleophilic demethylation of methyl o-alkoxyaryl ethers is accelerated relative to anisole [Benzene, methoxy-],[6] and this reaction is no exception. Lithium diphenylphosphide cleavage of anisole is complete in about 4 hours in refluxing tetrahydrofuran, whereas the present reaction is complete within 2 hours at 25°.

1. Department of Chemistry, California Institute of Technology, Pasadena, California 91109.
2. T. Kametani, H. Iida, and C. Kobayashi, J. Heterocycl. Chem., 7, 339 (1970).
3. F. G. Mann and M. J. Pragnell, J. Chem. Soc., 4120 (1965).
4. R. E. Ireland and S. Welch, J. Amer. Chem. Soc., 92, 7232 (1970).
5. Gloria Pfister, unpublished results, this laboratory.
6. G. I. Feutrill and R. N. Mirrington, Aust. J. Chem., 25, 1719, 1731 (1972).

5,6-DIHYDRO-2H-PYRAN-2-ONE AND 2H-PYRAN-2-ONE

$$+ \; CH_2O \; \xrightarrow[\text{CH}_3\text{CO}_2\text{H, reflux}]{\text{H}_2\text{SO}_4}$$

$$\xrightarrow[\text{CCl}_4,\ \text{reflux}]{\substack{\text{N-bromosuccinimide} \\ \text{dibenzoyl peroxide}}} \quad \xrightarrow[\text{reflux}]{(\text{C}_2\text{H}_5)_3\text{N}}$$

Submitted by M. Nakagawa,[1] J. Saegusa,[1]
M. Tonozuka,[1] M. Obi,[1] M. Kiuchi,[1]
T. Hino,[1] and Y. Ban[2]
Checked by A. Wick, D. Ehrlich, and A. Brossi

1. Procedure

A. *5,6-Dihydro-2H-pyran-2-one* [*2H-Pyran-2-one, 5,6-dihydro-*]. In a 500-ml., one-necked, round-bottomed flask equipped with a reflux condenser are combined 43 g. (0.50 mole) of vinylacetic acid [3-Butenoic acid] (Note 1), 30 g. (1 mole) of paraformaldehyde (Note 2), 3 ml. of concentrated sulfuric acid, and 125 ml. of glacial acetic acid. This mixture is refluxed gently for 3 hours and then cooled to room temperature and swirled while 16 g. of anhydrous sodium acetate [Acetic acid, sodium salt] is added. Acetic acid is removed under reduced pressure at 50–55° on a rotary evaporator, 100 ml. of water is added, and the flask is fitted with a two-necked adapter, a thermometer, and a magnetic stirring bar. The flask is then immersed in an ice bath, and the solution is brought to pH 8 with aqueous 20% sodium hydroxide (Note 3), which is added dropwise and with stirring at a rate such that the temperature remains below 5°. The resulting solution is transferred to a 1-l. separatory funnel and extracted with four 300-ml. portions of dichloromethane (Note 4). After being washed with one 150-ml. portion of saturated aqueous sodium chloride (Note 5), the combined organic extracts are dried over anhydrous sodium sulfate and filtered. Removal of dichloromethane with a rotary evaporator leaves a mobile yellow oil, which is distilled under reduced pressure to give 12.3 g. (25.1%) of 5,6-dihydro-2H-pyran-2-one, b.p. 114–117° (18–19 mm.) (Note 6).

49

B. *2H-Pyran-2-one.* A mixture of 9.81 g. (0.100 mole) of 5,6-dihydro-2*H*-pyran-2-one, 200 mg. of benzoyl peroxide, 18.6 g. (0.105 mole) of *N*-bromosuccinimide [2,5-Pyrrolidinedione, 1-bromo-] (Note 7), and 800 ml. of carbon tetrachloride is prepared in a 2-l., three-necked, round-bottomed flask equipped with a reflux condenser and a mechanical stirrer. The resulting suspension is stirred and heated to reflux. After 1.5 hours at reflux, most of the solid is dissolved, and the solution gives a negative test with starch–iodide paper. The reaction mixture is then allowed to cool, during which time succinimide [2,5-Pyrrolidinedione] crystallizes out. The precipitate is removed by filtration, and the filtrate is concentrated under reduced pressure to leave crude 5-bromo-5,6-dihydro-2*H*-pyran-2-one [2*H*-Pyran-2-one, 5-bromo-5,6-dihydro] as an oil.

This residue is stirred at room temperature while 150 ml. of triethylamine [Ethanamine, *N,N*-diethyl] (Note 8) is added. Triethylamine hydrobromide begins to precipitate soon after the addition is started, and the resulting slurry is refluxed gently for 15 minutes. It is then cooled to room temperature, and the insoluble material is removed by filtration and washed with benzene. Concentration of the combined filtrates under reduced pressure leaves an oily residue, which is dissolved in 600 ml. of ether. The ethereal solution is transferred to a 1-l. separatory funnel, washed with two 20-ml. portions of saturated aqueous sodium chloride, dried over anhydrous sodium sulfate, and filtered. Ether is removed with a rotary evaporator, and the resulting oil is distilled at reduced pressure. A forerun of 265 mg. is collected below 103° (22 mm.), and then 6.7 g. (70%) of 2*H*-pyran-2-one distils as a colorless oil, b.p. 103–111° (19–22 mm.) (Note 9).

2. Notes

1. Vinylacetic acid is available from Tokyokasei Company, Ltd., Japan or from Fluka AG, Buchs, Switzerland. Commercial material, which shows about 3% of crotonic acid [2-Butenoic acid, (*E*)-] in its proton magnetic resonance spectrum, was distilled at 90–92° (40–43 mm.) prior to use.

2. The submitters obtained paraformaldehyde from Koso Chemical Company, Inc., Japan.

3. About 180 ml. is required.

4. In these extractions, the organic layer is the lower one. If the two

phases do not separate readily, fine-grained precipitates are probably at fault. These may be removed by filtration through a Büchner funnel.

5. Excess washing should be avoided, since 5,6-dihydro-2H-pyran-2-one is fairly soluble in water.

6. A forerun of approximately 180 mg. is collected below 110° (18 mm.). The infrared spectrum of this material is practically identical with that of the main distillate. Reported physical constants for 5,6-dihydro-2H-pyran-2-one are: b.p. 110° (15 mm.) and n_D^{25} 1.4730.[3]

7. The submitters obtained N-bromosuccinimide from Nakarai Chemicals Ltd., Japan, and crystallized it from water prior to use (m.p. 168–175°).

8. Triethylamine was purified by treatment with p-toluenesulfonyl chloride [Benzenesulfonyl chloride, 4-methyl-] and distillation.

9. The infrared spectrum of this material was essentially identical to that of the redistillate, b.p. 115–118° (37 mm.). Reported physical constants for 2H-pyran-2-one are: b.p. 206–209° (atmospheric pressure), n_D^{25} 1.5272,[7] and b.p. 110° (26 mm.), n_D^{25} 1.5270.[8]

3. Discussion

5,6-Dihydro-2H-pyran-2-one has been prepared by reductive cyclization of 5-hydroxy-2-pentynoic acid [2-Pentynoic acid, 5-hydroxy-], which is obtained in two steps from acetylene [Ethyne] and ethylene oxide [Oxirane];[3] and by the reaction of dihydropyran [2H-Pyran, 3,4-dihydro-] with singlet oxygen [Oxygen, singlet].[4,5] 2H-Pyran-2-one has been prepared by pyrolysis of heavy metal salts of coumalic acid [2H-Pyran-5-carboxylic acid, 2-oxo-],[6] by pyrolysis of α-pyrone-6-carboxylic acid [2H-Pyran-6-carboxylic acid, 2-oxo-] over copper,[7] and by pyrolysis of coumalic acid over copper (66–70% yield).[8]

The present one-step procedure for preparation of 5,6-dihydro-2H-pyran-2-one is slightly modified from that described in the original paper.[9] It is simpler and easier than the three-step method[3] used in the past and represents the most convenient synthesis presently available. The present preparation of 2H-pyran-2-one has several advantages compared to the alternatives mentioned above: simplicity of apparatus and technique, mild reaction conditions, availability of reactants, and ease of product isolation.

1. Faculty of Pharmaceutical Sciences, Chiba University, Chiba, Japan.
2. Faculty of Pharmaceutical Sciences, Hokkaido University, Sapporo, Japan.

ORGANIC SYNTHESES—VOL. 56

3. L. J. Haynes and E. R. H. Jones, *J. Chem. Soc. London*, 954 (1946).
4. P. D. Bartlett, G. D. Mendenhall, and A. P. Schaap, *Ann. N.Y. Acad. Sci.*, **171**, 79 (1970).
5. E. C. Blossey, *J. Amer. Chem. Soc.*, **95**, 5820 (1973).
6. H. von Pechmann, *Justus Liebigs Ann. Chem.*, **264**, 272 (1891).
7. J. Fried and R. C. Elderfield, *J. Org. Chem.*, **6**, 566 (1941).
8. H. E. Zimmerman, G. L. Grunewald, and R. M. Paudler, *Org. Syn.*, Coll. Vol. 5, 982 (1973).
9. M. Nakagawa, M. Tonozuka, M. Obi, M. Kiuchi, T. Hino, and Y. Ban, *Synthesis*, 510 (1974).

ENONE REDUCTION–ENOLATE ALKYLATION SEQUENCE: 2-ALLYL-3-METHYLCYCLOHEXANONE

[Cyclohexanone, 3-methyl-2-(2-propenyl)-]

Submitted by Drury Caine,[1] Sam T. Chao,[1] and Homer A. Smith[2]
Checked by Mark E. Jason and Kenneth B. Wiberg

1. Procedure

Caution! Since liquid ammonia is to be used, this preparation should be carried out in a well-ventilated hood.

A 2-l., three-necked, round-bottomed flask is fitted with a mechanical stirrer (Note 1), a pressure-equalizing dropping funnel, and a two-necked Claisen adapter holding a Dewar condenser (in the offset neck) and an adapter with stopcock for introduction of ammonia (Note 2). The entire apparatus is flame-dried under a stream of nitrogen, which enters at the top of the Dewar condenser, and a positive pressure of nitrogen is maintained throughout the experiment (Note 3). Anhydrous ammonia (1 l.) is introduced into the flask in liquid form (Note 4), the condenser is filled with an acetone–dry ice slurry, and the inlet adapter is removed and replaced by a glass stopper. Stirring is begun, and the ammonia is dried by adding very small pieces of lithium (*ca.* 5 mg. each) until the blue color persists (Note 5). Stirring is continued throughout the following reaction sequence.

Freshly-cut lithium wire (2.77 g., 0.40 g.-atom) (Note 6) is introduced into the flask, and the metal is allowed to dissolve for 20 minutes. Then a solution prepared from 20.0 g. (0.182 mole) of 3-methylcyclohex-2-enone [2-Cyclohexen-1-one, 3-methyl-] (Note 7), 3.27 g. (0.182 mole) of water, and 400 ml. of anhydrous ether (Notes 8 and 9) is added dropwise over 60 minutes (Note 10). Ten minutes after completion of the addition, a solution of 65 g. (0.54 mole) of allyl bromide [1-Propene, 3-bromo-] (Note 11) in 150 ml. of anhydrous ether is added from the dropping funnel in a stream over 60 seconds (Note 12). Five minutes later 30 g. of solid ammonium chloride is added as rapidly as possible. Stirring is discontinued, the Dewar condenser is removed, and the ammonia is allowed to evaporate. A mixture of 300 ml. of ether and 300 ml. of water is added, and the reaction mixture is transferred to a separatory funnel and shaken. After separation of the ether layer, the aqueous layer is saturated with sodium chloride and extracted with two 100-ml. portions of ether. The combined ether extracts are washed with 100 ml. of aqueous 5% hydrochloric acid and 100 ml. of aqueous saturated sodium chloride and then dried over anhydrous magnesium sulfate. After filtration to remove the drying agent, ether is removed using a rotary evaporator. The residual oil is distilled through a 37-cm. column packed with 6-mm. Raschig rings and equipped with a resistance heater for thermal balance. There is a forerun, b.p. 74–80° (12 mm.), consisting principally of 3-methylcyclohexanone, and then 2-allyl-3-methylcyclohexanone distils as a 20:1 mixture of *trans*- and *cis*-isomers, b.p. 99–102° (12 mm.), n_D^{24} 1.4680–1.4683 (Note 13). The yield is 12.3–13.6 g. (45–49%) (Note 14).

2. Notes

1. A glass stirring shaft and blade should be employed.

2. An apparatus with four necks makes possible the introduction of solid reactants without removal of the condenser or dropping funnel.

3. An apparatus similar to that described by Johnson and Schneider[3] was used for maintaining a nitrogen atmosphere in the system. A positive nitrogen flow was maintained whenever the system was open.

4. Some commercial cylinders are provided with an eductor tube, which allows the extraction of liquid ammonia when the cylinder is

upright. Cylinders not so equipped may be secured in a suitable wooden or metal cradle, constructed so that the outlet valve is inclined below the body of the cylinder. The checkers dried commercial ammonia with sodium in a separate flask and then distilled the ammonia into the reaction flask.

5. Although water was used as a proton donor in this preparation, drying of the liquid ammonia and ether was carried out so that the lithium–ammonia solution would not be exposed to water during preparation and so that the amount of water added could be accurately controlled.

6. Lithium wire purchased from the Lithium Corporation of America, Inc. was used. The wire was cut in 2.5–5.0-cm. pieces, washed free of the protective oil with ether, and weighed by transferring quickly to a tared beaker containing mineral oil. The lengths of wire were again washed in a beaker of ether and then held with forceps over an open neck of the reaction flask (positive nitrogen flow), cut with scissors into 3–4-mm. pieces, and allowed to fall directly into the flask.

7. 3-Methylcyclohex-2-enone, b.p. 76–78° (11 mm.), was purchased from Aldrich Chemical Company, Inc. or prepared according to the procedure of Cronyn and Riesser.[4]

8. Ether was heated to reflux over lithium aluminum hydride and distilled prior to use.

9. The three-component mixture required a few minutes of shaking to ensure the formation of a homogeneous solution. It is essential that the water be completely dissolved before the solution is used.

10. The deep blue solution of lithium in liquid ammonia generally turned pale blue at the end of the addition, and a white precipitate of the lithium enolate and/or lithium hydroxide could be seen.

11. Allyl bromide purchased from Eastman Organic Chemicals, Inc. was dried over calcium chloride and distilled, b.p. 69–70° (760 mm.), prior to use.

12. Since the ammonia boils vigorously during this addition, it is advisable to open one neck of the flask to avoid excessive pressure buildup.

13. Infrared (neat) cm.$^{-1}$: 1714 ($C{=}O$), 1641 ($C{=}C$); proton magnetic resonance (CCl_4) δ, number of protons, multiplicity: 0.82 and 1.10 (total of 3, two doublets, CH_3 of *cis*- and *trans*-isomers, respectively), 1.4–2.7 (10, multiplet), 5.1 (2, two triplets, $-CH{=}CH_2$), 5.8 (1, multiplet, $-CH{=}CH_2$). The distillate was analyzed by gas chromatography on a 3 mm. by 2 m. column containing 10% Carbowax 20M

on HMDS Chromosorb W (60–80 mesh). Using a column temperature of 104° and a carrier gas flow rate of 30 ml./minute, the retention times for the *trans-* and *cis-*isomers were 9.0 minutes and 11.2 minutes, respectively. The product contained greater than 98% of the mixture of *trans-* and *cis-*2-allyl-3-methylcyclohexanone.

A portion of the product was heated to reflux with methanolic sodium methoxide to convert it into the thermodynamic mixture of *trans-* (*ca.* 65%) and *cis-* (*ca.* 35%) isomers. Small amounts of the isomers were collected by preparative gas chromatography using an 8 mm. by 1.7 m. column containing 15% Carbowax 20M on Chromosorb W, and each isomer exhibited the expected spectral and analytical properties. The same thermodynamic mixture of isomers was prepared independently by lithium–ammonia reduction[5] of 2-allyl-3-methylcyclohex-2-enone [2-Cyclohexen-1-one, 3-methyl-2-(2-propenyl)-],[6] followed by equilibration with methanolic sodium methoxide.

Using the 3 mm. by 2 m. gas chromatography column described above, a mixture of stereoisomers of 2-allyl-5-methylcyclohexanone [Cyclohexanone, 5-methyl-2-(2-propenyl)-], prepared by allylation of the enamine of 3-methylcyclohexanone,[7a] showed peaks at retention times of 8.4 minutes (more stable isomer) and 9.6 minutes. A mixture of the two isomeric 2-allyl-3-methylcyclohexanones and the two isomeric 2-allyl-5-methylcyclohexanones clearly exhibited four distinct peaks on gas chromatography.

14. The checkers obtained an additional 2–5 g. of 2-allyl-3-methylcyclohexanone by redistilling the column wash and the pot residue through a short-path distillation column. This raised the total yield to 14.9–18.1 g. (54–66%).

3. Discussion

Alternative preparations of 2-allyl-3-methylcyclohexanone include a) lithium–ammonia reduction of 2-allyl-3-methylcyclohex-2-enone (see Note 13), which can be prepared by alkylation of 3-methylcyclohex-2-enone or by alkylation of 4-carboethoxy-3-methylcyclohex-2-enone [Hagemann's ester; 2-Cyclohexene-1-carboxylic acid, 2-methyl-4-oxo-, ethyl ester], followed by hydrolysis and decarboxylation; and b) conjugate addition of lithium dimethylcuprate [Cuprate (1-), dimethyl-, lithium] to 2-cyclohexen-1-one followed by trapping of the enolate with allyl iodide[7b] or allyl bromide[7c] in an appropriate solvent.

The present procedure utilizes the enone reduction–enolate alkylation procedure discovered by Stork and co-workers,[8] which often provides a means of directing alkylation to relatively inaccessible α-positions of unsymmetrical ketones. This procedure has been applied to the synthesis of specifically alkylated steroidal ketones,[9] decalones,[8] hydrindanones,[8] and monocyclic[5] and acyclic ketones.[10] The method is successful because, unlike enolates with other alkali metal counterions, lithium enolates of unsymmetrical ketones undergo alkylation with relatively reactive alkylating agents more rapidly than they equilibrate to isomeric enolates by proton transfer.

The direct conversion of 3-methylcyclohex-2-enone into 2-allyl-3-methylcyclohexanone provides an interesting example of the utility of the reduction–alkylation procedure. Synthesis of this compound from 3-methylcyclohexanone would be difficult because the latter is converted mainly into 2-alkyl-5-methylcyclohexanones either by direct base-catalyzed alkylation[11] or by indirect methods such as alkylation of its enamine (see Note 13) or alkylation of the magnesium salt derived from its cyclohexylimine.[12]

The procedure may also be extended to other alkylating agents and enones. We have reported[5] that 2,3-dimethylcyclohexanone [Cyclohexanone, 2,3-dimethyl-] can be prepared by reduction–methylation of 3-methylcyclohex-2-enone and have found that 2-benzyl-3-methylcyclohexanone [Cyclohexanone, 3-methyl-2-(phenylmethyl)-] is obtained by substituting benzyl chloride [Benzene, (chloromethyl)-] for allyl bromide in a procedure similar to that described above but employing a longer alkylation time.[13] In a related case, Conia and Berlin[14] have prepared 2-methyl-3-(3-butenyl)cyclohexanone [Cyclohexanone, 3-(3-butenyl)-2-methyl-] by reduction–methylation of 3-(3-butenyl)cyclohex-2-enone [2-Cyclohexen-1-one, 3-(3-butenyl)-].

High-boiling products found in this procedure and in similar experiments involving cyclohex-2-enone derivatives[5] probably result from bimolecular reduction processes.[15] 3-Methylcyclohexanone, which arises by protonation rather than alkylation of the enolate (and which made up ca. 12% of the volatile products), is probably the result of reaction of allyl bromide with liquid ammonia to form the acidic species allyl ammonium bromide.[5,10]

Unless a proton donor is added, the lithium–ammonia reduction of an enone leads to the lithium enolate and lithium amide. The latter is a sufficiently strong base to rapidly convert the mono-alkylated ketone into its enolate, which can be further alkylated. The function of the

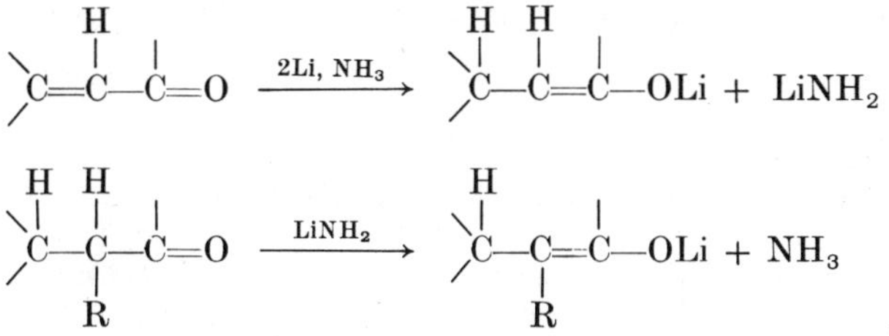

$$\underset{/}{\overset{\backslash}{C}}=\underset{\overset{|}{H}}{C}-\underset{\overset{|}{O}}{C}=O \quad \xrightarrow{\text{2Li, NH}_3} \quad \underset{/}{\overset{\backslash}{C}}-\underset{\overset{|}{H}}{C}=\underset{\overset{|}{H}}{C}-OLi + LiNH_2$$

$$\underset{/}{\overset{\backslash}{C}}-\underset{\overset{|}{R}}{\underset{\overset{|}{H}}{C}}-\underset{\overset{|}{H}}{C}=O \quad \xrightarrow{\text{LiNH}_2} \quad \underset{/}{\overset{\backslash}{C}}-\underset{\overset{|}{R}}{C}=\underset{\overset{|}{H}}{C}-OLi + NH_3$$

added proton donor is to buffer the system by reaction with the lithium amide. *tert*-Butyl alcohol has been widely used as a proton donor in lithium-ammonia reductions,[5,8,10] but lithium *tert*-butoxide is also a sufficiently strong base to cause a significant amount of polyalkylation in easily ionizable systems. In a procedure similar to that above but in which *tert*-butyl alcohol was substituted for water, 2,2- and/or 2,6-diallyl-3-methylcyclohexanone made up 15–20% of the volatile products. However, when water was used as the proton donor so that lithium hydroxide was the strongest base present during the alkylation step, the amount of diallyl product was 2% or less.

It is interesting that *trans*-2-allyl-3-methylcyclohexanone is by far the major product of this reduction–alkylation sequence, being formed in greater than the equilibrium ratio (see Note 13). The lithium enolate would be expected to exist in the two conformations shown below:

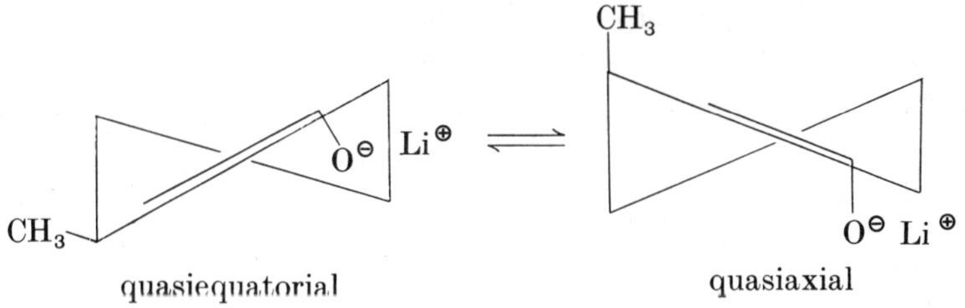

quasiequatorial   quasiaxial

The conformation having the methyl group quasiaxial may be quite important, because $A^{1,2}$-strain may be significant when the methyl group is quasiequatorial.[16] Recent work on the alkylation of lithium enolates of cyclohexanone derivatives has revealed that the stereochemistry of the reaction is governed largely by steric factors within the reactants.[17] From examination of models of the two conformations shown above, it appears that steric interactions between the methyl group and the approaching alkylating agent would be minimized in either of the two possible transition states which lead to the *trans* product.

1. School of Chemistry, Georgia Institute of Technology, Atlanta, Georgia 30332.
2. Department of Chemistry, Hampden-Sydney College, Hampden-Sydney, Virginia 23943.
3. W. S. Johnson and W. P. Schneider, *Org. Syn.*, Coll. Vol. **4**, 132 (1963).
4. M. W. Cronyn and G. H. Reisser, *J. Amer. Chem. Soc.*, **75**, 1664 (1953).
5. H. A. Smith, B. J. L. Huff, W. J. Powers, III, and D. Caine, *J. Org. Chem.*, **32**, 2851 (1967).
6. J. M. Conia and F. Rouessac, *Bull. Soc. Chim. Fr.*, 1925 (1963).
7. (a) S. K. Malhotra, D. F. Moakley, and F. Johnson, *Chem. Commun.*, 448 (1967); (b) R. K. Boeckman, Jr., *J. Org. Chem.*, **38**, 4450 (1973); (c) R. M. Coates and L. O. Sandefur, *J. Org. Chem.*, **39**, 277 (1974).
8. G. Stork, P. Rosen, N. L. Goldman, R. V. Coombs, and J. Tsuji, *J. Amer. Chem. Soc.*, **87**, 275 (1965).
9. C. Djerassi (ed.), "Steroid Reactions," Holden-Day, Inc., San Francisco, Ca., 1963, p. 322.
10. L. E. Hightower, L. R. Glasgow, K. M. Stone, D. A. Albertson, and H. A. Smith, *J. Org. Chem.*, **35**, 1881 (1970).
11. R. Cornubert and R. Humeau, *Bull. Soc. Chim. Fr.*, **49**, 1238 (1931).
12. G. Stork and S. R. Dowd, *J. Amer. Chem. Soc.*, **85**, 2178 (1963).
13. H. A. Smith, unpublished work.
14. J. M. Conia and P. Berlin, *Bull. Soc. Chim. Fr.*, 483 (1969).
15. (a) K. W. Bowers, R. W. Giese, J. Grimshaw, H. O. House, N. H. Kolodny, K. Kronberger, and D. K. Roe, *J. Amer. Chem. Soc.*, **92**, 2783 (1970); (b) H. O. House, R. W. Giese, K. Kronberger, J. P. Kaplan, and J. P. Simeone, *J. Amer. Chem. Soc.*, **92**, 2800 (1970).
16. F. Johnson, *Chem. Rev.*, **68**, 375 (1968).
17. (a) H. O. House, B. A. Tefertiller, and H. O. Olmstead, *J. Org. Chem.*, **33**, 935 (1968); (b) B. J. L. Huff, F. N. Tuller, and D. Caine, *J. Org. Chem.*, **34**, 3070 (1969).

ESTERIFICATION OF CARBOXYLIC ACIDS
WITH TRIALKYLOXONIUM SALTS:
ETHYL AND METHYL 4-ACETOXYBENZOATES

[Benzoic acid, 4-(acetyloxy)-, ethyl and methyl esters]

$$\text{R} = \text{CH}_3 \text{ or } \text{C}_2\text{H}_5$$

Submitted by Douglas J. Raber, Patrick Gariano, Jr.,
Albert O. Brod, Anne L. Gariano, and Wayne C. Guida[1]
Checked by H. Fliri and G. Büchi

1. Procedure

A. *Ethyl 4-Acetoxybenzoate.* A 100-ml., one-necked, round-bottomed flask is charged with 2.09 g. (0.011 mole) of triethyloxonium fluoborate [Oxonium, triethyl-, tetrafluoroborate(1−)] (Notes 1 and 2), 75 ml. of dichloromethane (Note 3), and 1.80 g. (0.010 mole) of 4-acetoxybenzoic acid [Benzoic acid, 4-(acetyloxy)-] (Note 4). A magnetic stirring bar is added, and the solution is stirred while 1.9 ml. (0.011 mole) of diisopropylethylamine [2-Propanamine, N-ethyl-N-(1-methylethyl)-] (Note 5) is introduced with a syringe (Note 6). The flask is then stoppered and allowed to stand at room temperature for 16–24 hours.

Work-up is initiated by extracting the reaction mixture with three 50-ml. portions of aqueous 1N hydrochloric acid, three 50-ml. portions of aqueous 1N potassium bicarbonate (Notes 7 and 8), and 50 ml. of saturated aqueous sodium chloride. The organic solution is then dried over sodium sulfate (Note 9), filtered, and concentrated on a rotary evaporator. Purification of the residue by bulb-to-bulb distillation (Note 10) at about 140° (5 mm.) provides 1.77–1.98 g. (85–95%) of ethyl 4-acetoxybenzoate as a colorless, viscous liquid (Note 11).

B. *Methyl 4-Acetoxybenzoate.* A 100-ml., one-necked, round-bottomed flask is charged with 1.63 g. (0.011 mole) of trimethyloxonium fluoborate [Oxonium, trimethyl-, tetrafluoroborate(1−)] (Notes 2 and 12), 75 ml. of dichloromethane (Notes 3 and 13), and 1.80 g. (0.010 mole) of 4-acetoxybenzoic acid (Note 4). A magnetic stirring bar is added, and the suspension is stirred while 1.9 ml. (0.011 mole) of diisopropylethyl-amine (Note 5) is introduced with a syringe (Note 6). The flask is then stoppered, and stirring is continued at room temperature for 16–24 hours, during which time all of the oxonium salt dissolves. Work-up exactly as that described in Part A is followed by bulb-to-bulb distilla-tion (Note 10) at about 140° (5 mm.) to provide 1.65–1.84 g. (85–95%) of methyl 4-acetoxybenzoate, m.p. 78–80° (Note 14).

2. Notes

1. Triethyloxonium fluoborate was prepared according to H. Meerwein, *Org. Syn.*, **46**, 113 (1966); Coll. Vol. **5**, 1080 (1973). The submitters stored this material at −20° under ether in a tightly-stoppered jar. They found that the use of a dry box or an inert atmosphere was not required in its handling. A sample of the oxonium salt–ether slurry was transferred to the tared reaction flask, ether was removed on a rotary evaporator, and the resulting solid was weighed and used without further purification. The checkers stored the dry oxonium salt under argon at −15°, maintained an argon atmosphere in all operations involving this reagent, and used dry solvent (Note 3). They consistently obtained 98% yields in two runs of Part A and two runs of Part B.

2. A 10% molar excess of the oxonium salt with regard to the carboxylic acid gives slightly higher yields than does an equimolar quantity.

3. The submitters used reagent-grade dichloromethane without purification. The checkers dried dichloromethane by distillation from phosphorous pentoxide.

4. This is prepared from 4-hydroxybenzoic acid and acetic anhydride following a procedure for 2-acetoxybenzoic acid.[2] The crude product is conveniently purified by stirring with chloroform (about 15 ml. per gram of acid) and removing any insoluble residue by filtration. Evapora-tion of the chloroform gives material melting at 186–188° (lit.[3] 189–190°).

5. This product was obtained from Aldrich Chemical Company, Inc. In many cases, the use of other amines may be satisfactory. Neverthe-

less, the use of a hindered base minimizes destruction of the oxonium salt by side reaction with the amine.

6. The use of a syringe affords a convenient method both for measuring the desired quantity of amine and adding it to the reaction mixture. In general, a mildly exothermic reaction takes place during addition of the amine. The submitters, working in an open vessel, suggest that if the reaction is scaled up or if the solution is more concentrated, care should be taken to add the amine gradually so that the reaction mixture does not boil over. For large-scale reactions they recommend the use of a dropping funnel. The checkers, working under argon and introducing the amine through a rubber septum, noted a considerable increase in pressure during the addition. Thus with this experimental setup a suitable pressure vent is required.

7. Any unreacted carboxylic acid may be recovered by neutralization and extraction of the bicarbonate solution.

8. In preparing ethers of phenols, aqueous $1N$ sodium hydroxide should be substituted for the sodium bicarbonate solution.

9. In many instances, the dichloromethane solution can be dried adequately by a simple filtration through coarse filter paper.

10. The "Kugelrohr" apparatus sold by Rinco Instrument Company, Inc. or any comparable bulb-to-bulb distillation apparatus is satisfactory. Fractional distillation is unnecessary.

11. The product crystallizes on standing overnight at $-20°$ and melts at 30–32°. Gas chromatographic analysis showed it to be at least 99% pure. Ethyl 4-acetoxybenzoate has been reported to melt at 34°.[4]

12. This compound was prepared according to T. J. Curphey, *Org. Syn.*, **51**, 142 (1971). The submitters and the checkers stored and handled this material using the techniques outlined for triethyloxonium fluoborate in Note 1.

13. Trimethyloxonium fluoborate is only slightly soluble in dichloromethane. However, the use of a two-phase mixture presents no difficulties in either experimental procedure or yield.

14. Gas chromatographic analysis showed this material to be at least 99% pure. The melting point of methyl 4-acetoxybenzoate has been reported[5] as 81–81.6°. In both their runs, the checkers obtained a distilled product which melted from 60° to 74°, resolidified at 74°, and then remelted at 78–79°. A sample recrystallized from hexane showed the same behavior.

3. Discussion

This procedure provides a convenient method for the esterification of a wide variety of carboxylic acids. The reaction proceeds smoothly with sterically hindered acids[6] and with acids which contain various functional groups. Esters are obtained in high purity using Kugelrohr distillation as the sole purification technique. In cases where traces of dichloromethane present no problems, the crude product is usually pure enough to be used directly in subsequent reactions. Methyl and ethyl ethers of phenols may also be prepared by this procedure (see Note 8).

Examples of polyfunctional carboxylic acids esterified by this method are shown in Table I. Yields are uniformly high, with the exception of those cases (maleic and fumaric acids) where some of the product appears to be lost during work-up as a result of water solubility. Even with carboxylic acids containing a second functional group (e.g., amide, nitrile) which can readily react with the oxonium salt, the more nucleophilic carboxylate anion is preferentially alkylated. The examples described in detail above illustrate the esterification of an acid containing a labile acetoxy group, which would not survive other procedures such as the traditional Fischer esterification.

The great utility of the trialkyloxonium salts is illustrated by the fact that high yields of esters are obtained using reagent which has been stored for up to 6 months under the submitters' conditions (Notes 1 and 12). Thus either trimethyl- or triethyloxonium fluoborate can be prepared in quantity, stored, and used for esterification as required.

Other examples of esterification with trialkyloxonium salts have been reported.[7,8] The present procedure offers the advantages that the reactive carboxylate ion is generated *in situ* and that a low-boiling, nonaqueous solvent is employed, whereby the experimental procedure is considerably simplified. A related method has been reported which utilizes a hindered amine with dimethyl sulfate [Sulfuric acid, dimethyl ester] as the alkylating agent.[9] The present procedure is carried out under somewhat milder conditions and avoids the use of highly toxic reagents.

The only other esterification method which rivals the present procedure in convenience, mildness of conditions, selectivity, and yield is the preparation of methyl esters with diazomethane [Methane, diazo-].[10] Esterification with trialkyloxonium salts, however, allows

TABLE I

Esterification of Carboxylic Acids with Trialkyloxonium Fluoborates

Acid	Triethyloxonium Fluoborate		Trimethyloxonium Fluoborate	
	Yield (%)[a]	Purity (%)[b]	Yield (%)[a]	Purity (%)[b]
CH_3 ... CO_2H, CH_3 ... CH_3 (trimethylbenzoic acid)	90	> 99	90	> 99
CO_2H (benzoic acid)	91	> 99	92	> 99
HO_2C, H / $C=C$ / H, CO_2H	77[c]	> 99	80[c]	> 99
HO_2C, CO_2H / $C=C$ / H, H	70[c]	> 99	74[c]	> 99
$N\equiv C-CH_2-CO_2H$	91	> 99	82	95
CO_2H, $C-N(C_2H_5)_2$, O	88	> 99	86	> 99
CO_2H, $O-C-CH_3$, O	89	95	85	> 99
CO_2H, $C-C_6H_5$, O	95	> 99	95	> 99

[a] Yield of distilled or crystallized ester.
[b] By glpc.
[c] In the esterification of dibasic acids a corresponding increase in equivalents of oxonium salt is employed; the product is the diester.

preparation of both methyl and ethyl esters and avoids the toxicity and explosion hazard[11] of diazomethane.

Furthermore, recent studies indicate that esterifications involving triethyloxonium fluoborate are often very rapid. For example, subsequent to the checking of this procedure the submitters have found that the reaction time of Part A may be shortened from 16–24 hours to 0.5 hour with no decrease in yield. The longer reaction time is still recommended for esterifications involving the trimethyl salt, such as that of Part B, because of the heterogeneous nature of the reaction mixture in these cases.

1. Department of Chemistry, University of South Florida, Tampa, Florida 33620.
2. A. I. Vogel, "A Textbook of Practical Organic Chemistry," 3rd ed., Longman, London, 1956, p. 996.
3. F. D. Chattaway, J. Chem. Soc., 2495 (1931).
4. D. Vorländer and W. Selke, Z. Phys. Chem. Abt. A, 129, 434 (1927) [C.A., 24, 4198 (1930)].
5. C. G. Mitton, R. L. Schowen, M. Gresser, and J. Shapley, J. Amer. Chem. Soc., 91, 2036 (1969).
6. D. J. Raber and P. Gariano, Tetrahedron Lett., 4741 (1971).
7. H. Meerwein, G. Hinz, P. Hofmann, E. Kroning, and E. Pfeil, J. Prakt. Chem., 147, 257 (1937).
8. T. Hamada and O. Yonemitsu, Chem. Pharm. Bull. Tokyo, 19, 1444 (1971).
9. F. H. Stodola, J. Org. Chem., 29, 2490 (1964).
10. L. F. Fieser and M. Fieser, "Reagents for Organic Synthesis," Vol. 1, John Wiley & Sons, Inc., New York, N.Y., 1967, p. 192.
11. T. J. DeBoer and H. J. Backer, Org. Syn., Coll. Vol. 4, 250 (1963).

ETHYL (E)-3-NITROACRYLATE

[2-Propenoic acid, 3-nitro-, ethyl ester, (E)-]

Submitted by JOHN E. McMURRY and JOHN H. MUSSER[1]
Checked by KYO OKADA, TSUTOMU AOKI,
and WATARU NAGATA

1. Procedure

Caution! Part A should be carried out in an efficient fume hood to protect the operator from poisonous NO_2 vapors.

A. *Ethyl 2-Iodo-3-nitropropionate* [*Propanoic acid, 2-iodo-3-nitro-, ethyl ester*]. A dry, 1-l., three-necked, round-bottomed flask is equipped with a magnetic stirring bar, a cold-finger condenser topped with a gas-inlet tube, and a rubber septum. The flask is flushed gently with nitrogen as 31 g. (0.122 mole) of iodine (Note 1), 45 ml. (0.41 mole) of ethyl acrylate [2-Propenoic acid, ethyl ester] (Notes 1 and 2), and 400 ml. of ether are added. The third neck is then stoppered, a 2-propanol–dry ice slurry is placed in the condenser, and the flask is immersed in an ice bath. After a brief pause to ensure thorough cooling, 9.5 ml. (0.166 mole) of dinitrogen tetroxide [Nitrogen oxide (N_2O_4)] is injected rapidly into the solution by syringe (Note 3). The reaction mixture is stirred for an hour at 0°, allowed to warm to room temperature, and stirred for a further 4 hours. It is then poured into a 1-l. separatory funnel and washed with saturated aqueous sodium thiosulfate [Thiosulfuric acid ($H_2S_2O_3$), disodium salt] until the ether layer is light yellow. After further washing with saturated aqueous sodium bicarbonate and saturated brine, the ether phase is dried over anhydrous sodium sulfate, filtered, and concentrated with a rotary evaporator. Unreacted ethyl acrylate is removed by exposing the residue to high vacuum (0.5 mm.) at room temperature (Note 4), which leaves 65.8 g. (98%) of ethyl 2-iodo-3-nitropropionate, n_D^{20} 1.5039 (Note 5).

B. *Ethyl 3-Nitroacrylate.* A solution of 65.8 g. (0.24 mole) of ethyl 2-iodo-3-nitropropionate in 400 ml. of ether is placed in a 1-l., three-necked, round-bottomed flask fitted with a mechanical stirrer and a reflux condenser topped with a gas-inlet tube. Powdered anhydrous sodium acetate [Acetic acid, sodium salt] (30 g., 0.37 mole) (Note 6) is added, the flask is flushed with nitrogen, and the reaction mixture is refluxed for 3 hours with vigorous stirring. After cooling, the ethereal solution is decanted from the sodium acetate into a 1-l. separatory funnel, where it is washed with 50 ml. of saturated aqueous sodium thiosulfate solution, 100 ml. of saturated sodium bicarbonate, and 50 ml. of brine. After drying over anhydrous sodium sulfate, the solution is sucked rapidly through a fritted-glass filter funnel containing 30 g. of neutral alumina (Note 7). Concentration of the filtrate on a rotary evaporator gives 32.0 g. (92%) of ethyl (*E*)-3-nitroacrylate, n_D^{20} 1.4570. This material crystallizes on refrigeration and is sufficiently pure for most applications (Note 8). Recrystallization from pentane at 0° to −15° affords 28.6 g. (83%) of spectrally pure material, m.p. 26–26.5° (Note 9).

2. Notes

1. The submitters used the following reagents as supplied: iodine, ether, and sodium acetate from Mallinckrodt Chemical Works, dinitrogen tetroxide from Matheson Gas Company, and ethyl acrylate from Aldrich Chemical Company, Inc. The checkers obtained dinitrogen tetroxide from Matheson Gas Company and the other reagents from Wako Pure Chemical Industries, Ltd., Japan.

2. Ethyl acrylate is used in approximately 50% molar excess over the expensive, limiting reagent, iodine. Use of an equimolar amount results in a lower yield (85%). The checkers distilled the reagent at 20° (39 mm.) prior to use.

3. Slower introduction of the dinitrogen tetroxide, by either dropwise addition of an ether solution or entrainment in a slow stream of nitrogen, gave similar results. The direct injection method was found to be easiest. The checkers distilled dinitrogen tetroxide at atmospheric pressure (b.p. 21°) prior to use.

4. The checkers found that some product codistilled with ethyl acrylate under these conditions, lowering their yield of pure ethyl 2-iodo-3-nitropropionate to 85–87%. They were able to obtain the submitters' yield, however, by introducing a slight modification. The flask containing the residue was fitted with an ice water condenser, and vacuum was applied at the top of the condenser. Evacuation at room temperature (0.5 mm.) for 3 hours removed the ethyl acrylate completely with no loss of product.

5. Distillation is unnecessary since the product is pure by spectral criteria. Infrared (liquid film) cm.$^{-1}$: 1730, 1555; proton magnetic resonance (CDCl$_3$) δ, number of protons, multiplicity: 1.30 (3, triplet, CH$_2$C*H*$_3$), 4.30 (2, quartet, C*H*$_2$CH$_3$), 4.8–5.2 (3, multiplet).

6. Sodium acetate must be ground to a fine powder and dried overnight at 120° to ensure reproducible elimination of hydroiodic acid.

7. This rapid filtration through alumina serves to eliminate minor colored impurities.

8. The product is best stored in a refrigerator, where it is stable for months. The submitters obtained highly pure material at this point, but the checkers always noted small amounts of impurities in their product. Crystallization was therefore carried out as described in the text. Distillation [b.p. 85–90° (15 mm.)] is impractical, because much of the product is lost due to decomposition in the stillpot.

9. Infrared (liquid film) cm.$^{-1}$: 3120 weak, 1730 strong; proton magnetic resonance (CDCl$_3$) δ, number of protons, multiplicity, coupling constant J in Hz.: 1.35 (3, triplet, CH$_2$C*H*$_3$), 4.30 (2, quartet, C*H*$_2$CH$_3$), 7.02 and 7.69 (1 each, AB quartet, $J = 14$, olefinic C*H*).

3. Discussion

This procedure for the synthesis of ethyl 3-nitroacrylate is essentially that of Stevens and Emmons.[2] Four major changes have been introduced by the submitters: rapid introduction of dinitrogen tetroxide; no purification of the intermediate nitro iodo ester; use of dry, finely powdered sodium acetate for elimination of hydroiodic acid; and percolation of the final product through a mat of alumina. With these modifications, the preparation is reproducible and highly efficient (80–90% overall).

Ethyl 3-nitroacrylate is an extremely reactive receptor in the Michael reaction. It has found use in the synthesis of the α-methylenebutyrolactone moiety[3] characteristic of many sesquiterpenes, as shown below. It should also be a powerful dienophile in the Diels-Alder reaction, although this aspect of its chemistry has not been investigated in detail.

1. Natural Sciences I, University of California, Santa Cruz, California 95064.
2. T. E. Stevens and W. D. Emmons, *J. Amer. Chem. Soc.*, **80**, 338 (1958).
3. J. W. Patterson and J. E. McMurry, *Chem. Commun.*, 488 (1971).

FREE-RADICAL ALKYLATION OF QUINONES: 2-PHENOXYMETHYL-1,4-BENZOQUINONE

[2,5-Cyclohexadiene-1,4-dione, 2-(phenoxymethyl)-]

Submitted by NIELS JACOBSEN [1]
Checked by R. J. DeFRANCO and R. E. BENSON

1. Procedure

In a 250-ml., three-necked flask fitted with a mechanical stirrer, a thermometer, and a 25-ml., graduated, pressure-equalizing dropping funnel are placed 7.60 g. (0.050 mole) of phenoxyacetic acid [Acetic acid, phenoxy-] (Note 1), 5.40 g. (0.050 mole) of 1,4-benzoquinone [2,5-Cyclohexadiene-1,4-dione] (Note 2), 1 g. (0.006 mole) of silver nitrate [Nitric acid silver(1+) salt] (Note 3), and 125 ml. of water (Note 4). The mixture is then stirred and heated to 60–65° by means of a heating mantle until dissolution is complete. The resulting solution is stirred vigorously while a solution of 13.7 g. (0.060 mole) of ammonium peroxydisulfate [Peroxydisulfuric acid ([(HO)S(O)$_2$]$_2$O$_2$), diammonium salt] (Note 5) in 25 ml. of water is added at a rate of 0.5 ml. per minute for the first 40 minutes and then at a rate of 0.25 ml. per minute for the last 20 minutes. Throughout the addition, the reaction mixture is maintained at 60–65° (Notes 6 and 7).

After the addition is complete the mixture is stirred for 5 minutes at 65° and then cooled to 5–10° in an ice bath. The precipitated solid is collected by suction filtration (Note 8), washed with 50 ml. of cold water, and pressed to remove most of the liquid. Inorganic contaminants, usually present in small amounts, are removed by dissolving the solid in 350 ml. of boiling acetone and filtering the hot solution through fluted filter paper. Concentration of the filtrate on a rotary evaporator gives a dark red crude product (10.5–11.4 g.), which is dissolved in 220–240 ml. of boiling 95% ethanol. On cooling the solution to 5°, the alkylated quinone crystallizes in brownish-yellow needles, which are collected by filtration and air-dried to 6.7–8.0 g., m.p. 135–137°. Recrystallization from 30 ml. of ethanol per gram of product gives 6.6–7.4 g. (61–69%) of 2-phenoxymethyl-1,4-benzoquinone, m.p. 137–138° (Note 9).

2. Notes

1. The submitter used Fluka *puriss*-grade phenoxyacetic acid. The checkers used material available from Eastman Organic Chemicals.

2. The submitter used Fluka *purum*-grade benzoquinone that was recrystallized once from petroleum ether (b.p. 60°) and had m.p. 111–113°. The checkers used Fisher purified-grade material without recrystallization.

3. The submitter used reagent-grade silver nitrate available from Merck & Company, Inc.

4. In the case of a water-insoluble quinone or carboxylic acid, acetonitrile can be used as cosolvent.[2]

5. Fluka *purum*-grade ammonium peroxydisulfate was used by the submitter. The checkers used ACS reagent-grade material available from Fisher Scientific Company.

6. The reaction is slightly exothermic, but it is necessary to heat the mixture occasionally in order to maintain it at 60–65°.

7. The checkers found that increasing the addition rate of persulfate solution to 1.5 ml. per minute, while giving a somewhat lower initial

TABLE I

Substituted Quinones Derived by Alkylation

Parent Quinone	Acid	Derived Substituted Quinone	Yield (%)[a]	Reference
1,4-Benzoquinone	Pivalic [Propanoic acid, 2,2-dimethyl-]	2-tert-Butyl [2,5-Cyclohexadiene-1,4-dione, 2-(1,1-dimethylethyl)-]	67[b]	2
1,4-Benzoquinone	Phenylacetic [Benzeneacetic acid]	2-Benzyl [2,5-Cyclohexadiene-1,4-dione, 2-(phenylmethyl)-]	87	2
1,4-Benzoquinone	α-Chloropropionic [Propanoic acid, 2-chloro-]	2-(α-Chloroethyl) [2,5-Cyclohexadiene-1,4-dione, 2-(1-chloroethyl)-]	45[b]	2
1,4-Naphthoquinone [1,4-Naphthalenedione]	Methoxyacetic [Acetic acid, methoxy-]	2-Methoxymethyl [1,4-Naphthalenedione, 2-(methoxymethyl)-]	50	2
1,4-Naphthoquinone	Adipic [Hexanedioic acid]	2-(ω-Carboxybutyl) [2-Naphthalenepentanoic acid, 1,4-dihydro-1,4-dioxo-]	51	2
2-Methyl-1,4-naphthoquinone [1,4-Naphthalenedione, 2-methyl-]	Cyclopropanecarboxylic [Cyclopropanecarboxylic acid]	2-Cyclopropyl-3-methyl [1,4-Naphthalenedione, 2-cyclopropyl-3-methyl-]	37	3
2-Acetoxy-1,4-naphthoquinone [1,4-Naphthalenedione, 2-(acetyloxy)-]	4-Methyl-3-pentenoic [3-Pentenoic acid, 4-methyl-]	2-Acetoxy-3-(γ,γ-dimethylallyl) [1,4-Naphthalenedione, 2-(acetyloxy)-3-(3-methyl-2-butenyl)-]	73	4

[a] Yields are based on the parent quinone.
[b] Modified procedure (see Discussion).

70

yield (62% after one recrystallization), resulted in a product of sufficient purity (m.p. 137–138°) as to require no further recrystallization.

8. This work-up procedure applies only when the crude product can be crystallized from the reaction mixture. If the product is partly soluble in the reaction medium or if it separates as a gum, an extraction procedure is employed.

9. Infrared ($CHCl_3$) cm.$^{-1}$: 1660 strong, 1600 medium, 1590 medium; ultraviolet (95% ethanol) nm. max. (ϵ): 220 (12,700), 248 (18,600), 269 shoulder, 276 shoulder; proton magnetic resonance ($CDCl_3$) δ, number of protons, multiplicity, coupling constant J in Hz.: 4.9 (2, doublet, $J = 2$, CH_2O), 6.7–7.5 (8, multiplet).

3. Discussion

The procedure described above has been used to prepare various alkylated 1,4-benzoquinones and 1,4-napthoquinones,[2,3] including some naturally occurring quinones.[4] A few examples are listed in Table I to show the scope of the method.

The reaction is a free-radical alkylation in which radicals are derived from a carboxylic acid by decarboxylation with $Ag^+/S_2O_8^{2-}$. It has the advantage that the reaction medium can be adjusted so that the monoalkylated product precipitates as it is formed, whereby di- or polyalkylation[5] is suppressed.

The reaction fails if the decarboxylation produces a radical that is easily oxidized, such as an α-hydroxyalkyl radical.[2] In intermediate cases, such as tert-alkyl or α-alkoxyalkyl radicals,[2] the yield based on the parent quinone is usually improved by using an excess of persulfate and carboxylic acid to compensate for the loss of radicals due to oxidation (footnote b, Table I).

1. Department of Organic Chemistry, University of Aarhus, 8000 Aarhus C, Denmark.
2. N. Jacobsen and K. Torssell, Justus Liebigs Ann. Chem., 763, 135 (1972).
3. J. Goldman, N. Jacobsen, and K. Torssell, Acta Chem. Scand., 28, 492 (1974).
4. N. Jacobsen and K. Torssell, Acta Chem. Scand., 27, 3211 (1973).
5. B. M. Bertilsson, B. Gustafsson, I. Kühn, and K. Torssell, Acta Chem. Scand., 24, 3590 (1970).

INDOLES FROM ANILINES:
ETHYL 2-METHYLINDOLE-5-CARBOXYLATE

[1*H*-Indole-5-carboxylic acid, 2-methyl, ethyl ester]

$$CH_3\overset{O}{\overset{\|}{C}}CH_2Cl + CH_3SNa \xrightarrow[\text{5°, then 25°}]{CH_3OH} CH_3\overset{O}{\overset{\|}{C}}CH_2SCH_3$$

Submitted by P. G. GASSMAN and T. J. VAN BERGEN[1]
Checked by J. L. BELLETIRE and G. BÜCHI

1. Procedure

Caution! Part A must be conducted in an efficient hood to avoid exposure to methanethiol and chloroacetone, both of which are highly irritating. In Part C, the usual precautions associated with the pyrophoric reagent Raney nickel (Note 12) should be observed.

A. *Methylthio-2-propanone [2-Propanone, 1-methylthio-].[2]* A 2-l., three-necked, round-bottomed flask is equipped with a sealed mechanical stirrer and a two-necked adapter holding a thermometer and a

condenser topped with a silica gel drying tube. After 700 ml. of anhydrous methanol has been added, the third neck is stoppered, and the
flask is immersed in an ice water bath. Stirring is begun, and 108 g.
(2.00 moles) of sodium methoxide [Methanol, sodium salt] (Note 1) is
added in small portions at a rate sufficiently gradual to prevent a large
exotherm (Note 2). When all of the methoxide has dissolved and the
temperature has returned to 5°, the stopper is replaced by a 200-ml.,
pressure-equalizing, jacketed addition funnel (Note 3). This funnel,
charged previously with 130 ml. (2.20 moles) of methanethiol (Note 4),
contains a dry ice–2-propanol slurry in the cooling jacket, and is topped
with a silica gel drying tube. Stirring and cooling are continued while
the methanethiol is run into the flask over a 20-minute period, and for
15 minutes thereafter. The jacketed addition funnel is then replaced by
a standard, 200-ml., pressure-equalizing addition funnel, which is used
to add 185 g. (2.00 moles) of chloroacetone [2-Propanone, 1-chloro-]
(Note 5) to the reaction mixture over 1 hour. When this addition is
complete, the ice bath is removed, and the suspension is stirred overnight at room temperature. The insoluble material, which is largely
inorganic salts, is removed by filtration through Celite, and the filter
cake is washed with two 150-ml. portions of absolute methanol. After
methanol has been removed from the combined filtrates by distillation,
the residue is distilled through a 300-mm. Vigreux column to yield
155–158 g. (74–76%) of methylthio-2-propanone, b.p. 153–154° (760
mm.), n_D^{23} 1.4728.

B. *Ethyl 2-Methyl-3-methylthioindole-5-carboxylate* [1*H-Indole-5-
carboxylic acid, 2-methyl-3-(methylthio)-, ethyl ester*]. A 1-l., three-
necked, round-bottomed flask is equipped with a sealed mechanical
stirrer, a 100-ml., pressure-equalizing addition funnel, and a two-necked
adapter holding a low-temperature thermometer and a gas-inlet tube.
The flask is charged with 16.5 g. (0.10 mole) of ethyl *p*-aminobenzoate
[Benzocaine; Benzoic acid, 4-amino, ethyl ester] (Note 6) and 500 ml. of
dichloromethane (Note 7), and a positive pressure of dry nitrogen is
established while the solution is stirred and cooled to −70° with a
2-propanol–dry ice bath. The resulting suspension is stirred vigorously,
and a solution of 10.8 g. (0.10 mole) of *tert*-butyl hypochlorite[3] [Hypo-
chlorous acid, 1,1-dimethylethyl ester] in 50 ml. of dichloromethane
(Note 7) is added dropwise over a 10-minute period. The reaction
mixture is stirred for 1 hour at −70°, followed by dropwise addition of
a solution of 10.4 g. (0.10 mole) of methylthio-2-propanone in 50 ml. of

dichloromethane (Note 7) during 10 minutes. A slight exotherm (*ca.* 5°) is noted during the addition, and a clear yellow solution results. After stirring for another hour at − 70°, during which time a suspension of precipitated salts forms, a solution of 10.1 g. (0.10 mole) of triethyl-amine [Ethanamine, *N,N*-diethyl-] (Note 8) in 30 ml. of dichloro-methane (Note 7) is added dropwise during 10 minutes. After a further 15 minutes at − 70°, the cooling bath is removed.

When the reaction mixture has warmed to room temperature, stirring is made more vigorous, and 100 ml. of water is added. The layers are separated, and the organic phase is dried over anhydrous magnesium sulfate and filtered. Removal of dichloromethane with a rotary evapo-rator leaves an oily residue, which is cooled in an ice bath to induce crystallization. The resulting solid is stirred with 50 ml. of ether for 30 minutes at 0° (Note 9), collected by filtration, and washed with 25 ml. of ether at 0°. Concentration of the filtrate to 15 ml. and chilling at *ca.* 5° overnight yields a second crop of crystalline product, bringing the total crude yield to 14.7–18.0 g. (59–73%), m.p. 120.5–124° (Note 10). Recrystallization from absolute ethanol (5 ml. per 2 g.) yields 12.8–17.5 g. (51–70%) of ethyl 2-methyl-3-methylthioindole-5-carboxylate, m.p. 125.5–127°.

C. *Ethyl 2-methylindole-5-carboxylate.* A solution of 10.0 g. (0.040 mole) of ethyl 2-methyl-3-methylthioindole-5-carboxylate in 300 ml. of absolute ethanol is placed in a 500-ml., three-necked, round-bottomed flask fitted with a mechanical stirrer. An excess (15 teaspoons) (Note 11) of freshly washed W-2 Raney nickel (Note 12) is added, and the mixture is stirred for one hour. Stirring is then stopped, the liquid phase is decanted, and the catalyst is washed twice by stirring for 15 minutes with 100-ml. portions of absolute ethanol and decanting the solvent. The combined ethanolic solutions are concentrated on a rotary evapo-rator, and the residual solid is dissolved in 150 ml. of warm dichloro-methane. This solution is dried over anhydrous magnesium sulfate and filtered, and the drying agent is washed with 40 ml. of dichloromethane. Concentration of the combined filtrates with a rotary evaporator gives 7.5–8.1 g. (93–99%) of ethyl 2-methylindole-5-carboxylate, m.p. 140.5–142.0° (Note 13).

2. Notes

1. Sodium methoxide was purchased from MC and B Manufacturing Chemists and used without further purification. Accurate weighing is

important, since the checkers noted that an excess of methoxide relative to chloroacetone, however slight, led to little or no product.

2. A convenient technique is to add the methoxide from an Erlenmeyer flask, connected to the previously stoppered neck of the reaction flask by a piece of flexible rubber tubing (Gooch tubing).

3. The addition funnel used in this preparation is depicted in Figure 1.

4. Methanethiol was purchased from Matheson Gas Products. *Caution! This compound has a powerful, vile odor, even at extremely low concentrations.* The gas, which liquefies at 6°, may be condensed by calibrating the addition funnel at 130 ml. with a grease pencil, inserting a cold-finger condenser topped with a gas-inlet tube in the female joint, and protecting the male joint from moisture by a drying tube. A dry ice–2-propanol slurry is placed in the condenser and the cooling jacket, and methanethiol is introduced through the gas inlet until the condensed liquid reaches the calibration mark.

5. Chloroacetone was purchased from Distillation Products (Eastman Organic Chemicals) and distilled prior to use. *Caution! This compound is an intensely powerful lachrymator.*

6. Ethyl *p*-aminobenzoate was purchased from the Aldrich Chemical Company, Inc. and used without further purification.

7. Commercial dichloromethane was distilled prior to use.

8. Triethylamine was purchased from the J. T. Baker Chemical Company and used without further purification.

9. If the ether is added prior to crystallization a slightly reduced yield of product results.

10. Occasionally the product is contaminated with an impurity (1–2%), which appears as tiny red needles. This material has been tentatively identified as diethyl azobenzene-4,4'-dicarboxylate [Benzoic acid, 4,4'-azobis-, diethyl ester].

11. A level teaspoonful contains about 3 g. of nickel.[4]

12. W-2 Raney nickel was purchased from W. R. Grace and Co. Prior to use it was washed with distilled water until neutral and then three times with absolute ethanol.[4] This material may ignite spontaneously if allowed to become dry. Thus in decanting, a small amount of solvent must be left behind to cover the catalyst. Spent catalyst is discarded by slurrying in water and flushing the slurry down the drain with running water.

13. Little change in melting point results when the product is recrystallized from benzene.

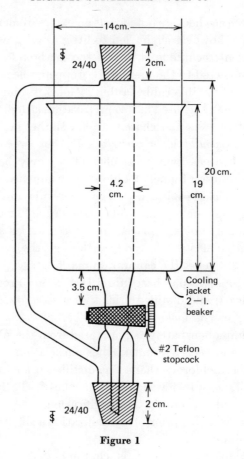

Figure 1

3. Discussion

This procedure is an example of a new indole synthesis, which can be utilized to prepare indoles substituted in the 1-, 2-, 4-, 5-, 6-, or 7-positions.[5] Indoles substituted on the phenyl ring with nitro, ethoxycarbonyl, chloro, methyl, and acetoxy groups have been prepared; hydrogen, methyl, and phenyl groups have been placed in the 2-position; and the method has been used to prepare 1-methylindoles. A similar procedure substituting α-thioesters for α-thioketones yields oxindoles in good overall yields.[6] The major advantages of this sequence are the availability of starting materials and the high overall yields of indoles and oxindoles realized.[7]

1. Department of Chemistry, The Ohio State University, Columbus, Ohio 43210.
2. C. K. Bradsher, F. C. Brown, and R. J. Grantham, *J. Amer. Chem. Soc.*, **76**, 114 (1954).
3. M. J. Mintz and C. Walling, *Org. Syn.*, **49**, 9 (1969).
4. R. Mozingo, *Org. Syn.*, Coll. Vol. **3**, 181 (1955).
5. P. G. Gassman and T. J. van Bergen, *J. Amer. Chem. Soc.*, **95**, 590 (1973).
6. P. G. Gassman and T. J. van Bergen, *J. Amer. Chem. Soc.*, **95**, 2718 (1973).
7. For a summary of other indole syntheses, see R. J. Sundberg, "The Chemistry of Indoles," Academic Press, Inc., New York, N.Y., 1970.

trans-IODOPROPENYLATION OF ALKYL HALIDES: (*E*)-1-IODO-4-PHENYL-2-BUTENE

[2-Butene, 1-iodo-4-phenyl, (*E*)-]

Submitted by KOICHI HIRAI and YUKICHI KISHIDA[1]
Checked by S. F. MARTIN and G. BÜCHI

1. Procedure

A. *2-Allylthio-2-thiazoline* [*Thiazole, 4,5-dihydro-2-(2-propenylthio)-*]. A solution of 11.9 g. (0.100 mole) of 2-mercapto-2-thiazoline [2-Thiazolidinethione] (Note 1) in 60 ml. of tetrahydrofuran is prepared in a 200-ml., one-necked, round-bottomed flask fitted with a 25-ml., pressure-equalizing dropping funnel. Allyl bromide [1-Propene, 3-bromo-] (12.1 g., 8.74 ml., 0.100 mole) is added in one portion at room temperature, and 5 minutes later 10.1 g. (13.9 ml., 0.100 mole) of triethylamine [Ethanamine, N,N-diethyl-] is added dropwise over a 10-minute period. After the dropping funnel has been replaced by a condenser, the mixture is refluxed gently for 4 hours. The resulting slurry is cooled and filtered to remove triethylamine hydrobromide, which is washed with 20 ml. of fresh tetrahydrofuran, and the combined organic solutions are concentrated with a rotary evaporator. The residue is dissolved in 100 ml. of ether, and this solution is washed with three 20-ml. portions of aqueous 5% potassium hydroxide and two 20-ml. portions of water. After drying over anhydrous magnesium sulfate, the ethereal solution is filtered free of drying agent and concentrated with a rotary evaporator. Vacuum distillation of the residue gives 10.9–11.1 g. (69–70%) of 2-allylthio-2-thiazoline, b.p. 51–54° (0.02 mm., bath temperature 75–80°, Note 2); n_D^{20} 1.5864 (Note 3).

B. *2-(4'-Phenyl-1'-buten-3'-yl)thio-2-thiazoline* [*Thiazole, 4,5-dihydro-2-[[1-(phenylmethyl)-2-propenyl]thio]-*]. A dry, 100-ml., four-necked, round-bottomed flask is fitted with a thermometer, a rubber septum, a pressure-equalizing dropping funnel, and a mechanical stirrer (Note 4). A positive pressure of nitrogen, applied either through an adapter inserted in the top of the funnel or through a needle inserted in the septum, is maintained throughout the reaction. A solution of 2.0 g. (0.0125 mole) of 2-allylthio-2-thiazoline in 24 ml. of dry tetrahydrofuran (Note 5) is placed in the flask, stirred vigorously, and cooled in an acetone–dry ice bath. When the internal temperature reaches $-55°$, 6.0 ml. (0.013 mole) of a 2.1 M n-butyllithium–n-hexane solution [Lithium, butyl-] (Note 6) is added by syringe at a rate such that the temperature remains below $-55°$; approximately 5 minutes is required. After stirring for an additional 20 minutes at $-55°$ to $-60°$, a solution of 2.15 g. (0.0125 mole) of benzyl bromide [Benzene, (bromomethyl)-] (Note 7) in 2 ml. of dry tetrahydrofuran is added at a rate such that the temperature remains below $-55°$, which again requires approximately 5 minutes. The solution is stirred for another 50 minutes at $-55°$ to $-60°$, allowed to warm to 0° during 30 minutes, and poured onto 70 ml. of ice water. The resulting mixture is extracted with three 25-ml. portions of ethyl acetate, and the extracts are combined, washed with two 15-ml. portions of saturated aqueous sodium chloride, and dried over anhydrous magnesium sulfate.

Removal of solvent from the extracts leaves a residue that is purified by dry-column chromatography.[2] The residue is dissolved in 40 ml. of acetone in a 300-ml., round-bottomed flask, 30 g. of silica gel (Note 8) is added, and the acetone is removed with a rotary evaporator. The resulting solid mixture is placed on top of 360 g. of dry silica gel (Note 8) packed in flexible nylon tubing (Note 9), and the column is developed with 420 ml. of 10:1 (*v*/*v*) benzene–acetone. Approximately 150 ml. of solvent drips from the bottom of the column toward the end of development, and this eluent is collected in 25-ml. fractions and checked for product by thin layer chromatography (Note 10). The column itself is then cut into 2-cm. sections, the silica gel in each section is eluted with three 25-ml. portions of ethyl acetate, and the eluent from each section is analyzed by thin-layer chromatography (Note 10). Combination of all the product-containing fractions yields 1.2–1.5 g. (40–47%) of the benzylated compound as an oil, n_D^{20} 1.6083 (Notes 11 and 12).

C. (*E*)-1-*Iodo*-4-*phenyl*-2-*butene*. In a 20-ml., round-bottomed flask are placed 2.0 g. (0.008 mole) of 2-(4'-phenyl-1'-buten-3'-yl)thio-2-thiazoline, 5 ml. of methyl iodide [Methane, iodo-], and 2 ml. of dimethylformamide. The resulting solution is heated at 75–80° for 2.5 hours under a nitrogen atmosphere (Note 13), cooled, and poured into 10 ml. of water. Extraction with three 12-ml. portions of ether separates the product from water-soluble by-products. The extracts are combined, washed with 8 ml. of 1% aqueous sodium thiosulfate and two 8-ml. portions of water, dried over anhydrous magnesium sulfate, and filtered to remove the drying agent. Removal of ether by distillation at 30° (100 mm.) leaves 1.5–1.7 g. (74–82%) of (*E*)-1-iodo-4-phenyl-2-butene (Notes 14 and 15).

2. Notes

1. This product was purchased from the Aldrich Chemical Company, Inc. and used without further purification.

2. Rapid distillation is required to avoid a [3,3]-sigmatropic rearrangement, which gives *N*-allylthiazolidine-2-thione [2-Thiazolidinethione, 3-(2-propenyl)-].

3. Infrared (neat) cm.$^{-1}$: 1570, 995, 965, 920; proton magnetic resonance ($CDCl_3$) δ, number of protons, multiplicity, coupling constant J in Hz.: 3.39 (2, triplet, $J = 7$, ring CH_2), 3.75 (2, doublet, $J = 6$,

allyl CH_2), 4.20 (2, triplet, $J = 7$, ring CH_2), 5.0–5.4 (2, multiplet, CH=CH_2), 5.6–6.3 (1, multiplet, CH=CH$_2$).

4. A three-necked flask may be used if magnetic stirring is substituted for mechanical stirring or if benzyl bromide is added with a syringe instead of a dropping funnel.

5. Tetrahydrofuran was distilled from lithium aluminum hydride immediately prior to use. See *Org. Syn.*, Coll. Vol. **5**, 976–977 (1973) for precautions.

6. This product was purchased from Sankyo Kasei, Inc., Tokyo (submitters) and Ventron Corporation (checkers).

7. This product was purchased from the Aldrich Chemical Company, Inc. and distilled prior to use, b.p. 126–128° (80 mm.).

8. Silica gel Woelm for dry-column chromatography, activity III/30 mm. [according to Brockmann and Schodder, *Ber.*, **74B**, 73 (1941)], was supplied by M. Woelm, Eschwege, Germany.

9. Woelm nylon column DCC-5 was used, giving a packed column of silica gel 66–67 cm. high and 32 mm. in diameter.

10. Merck precoated silica gel F$_{254}$ plates, layer thickness 0.25 mm., were used. Developing with 10:1 (v/v) benzene–acetone and visualizing with ultraviolet light, the product appears at Rf 0.58–0.67. Normally the product is found in the lower third of the column, and occasionally some is found in the last fractions of eluent collected during development. However, since the exact position of this material on the column depends critically on the way in which the column is packed, a thorough check of all fractions is advisable.

11. Infrared (neat) cm.$^{-1}$: 1570, 995, 965, 920, 740, 700; proton magnetic resonance (CDCl$_3$) δ, number of protons, multiplicity, coupling constant J in Hz.: 2.9–3.4 (4, multiplet, ring CH_2 and C$_6$H$_5$CH_2), 4.14 (2, triplet, $J = 8$, ring CH_2), 4.3–4.7 (1, multiplet, C=C—CHS—), 4.9–5.3 (2, multiplet, H_2C=CH—), 5.5–6.2 (1, multiplet, H_2C=CH—), 7.23 (5, broad singlet, aryl CH).

12. The submitters also tried to purify the crude product by distillation (130–145° at 0.005 mm.), but under these conditions decomposition took place. It is possible to substitute thick-layer chromatography for the dry column. Using Merck silica gel F$_{254}$ precoated plates, layer thickness 2 mm., and developing with 10:1 (v/v) benzene–acetone, the submitters report a 73% yield of pure product.

13. *N*-Methyl-2-methylthiothiazolium iodide [Thiazolium, 4,5-dihydro-3-methyl-2-(methylthio)-, iodide] (m.p. 132°) usually precipitates as the reaction proceeds.

14. (*E*)-1-Iodo-4-phenyl-2-butene is reported to decompose on attempted distillation at 4 mm.[3] The crude product, which is suitable for subsequent reactions (see Note 15), may be purified by thick-layer chromatography. Using the plates described in Note 10 and developing with hexane, the product is found at *Rf* 0.5 as an oil, n_D^{20} 1.5940; infrared (neat) cm.$^{-1}$: 1655 weak, 1600 medium, 1460 strong, 1150 strong, 960 strong (*trans*-CH=CH—), 740 strong, 690 strong; proton magnetic resonance (CDCl$_3$) δ, number of protons, multiplicity: 3.2–3.5 (2, multiplet, C$_6$H$_5$C*H*$_2$), 3.7–4.0 (2, multiplet, C*H*$_2$I), 5.6–5.9 (2, multiplet, vinylic C*H*), 7.23 (5, broad singlet, aryl C*H*).

15. This material may be converted directly to a phosphonium salt: 1.40 g. (0.0054 mole) of the crude iodide is dissolved in 20 ml. of benzene, and 1.42 g. (0.0054 mole) of triphenylphosphine [Phosphine, triphenyl-] is added. On standing, 2.5 g. (77%) of the triphenylphosphonium salt precipitates as a colorless 1:1 complex with benzene, m.p. 135–137°. Recrystallization from methanol–benzene raises the melting point to 140–142°. Analysis calculated for C$_{28}$H$_{29}$PI·C$_6$H$_6$: C, 68.23; H, 5.39. Found: C, 68.15; H, 5.28.

3. Discussion

(*E*)-1-Iodo-4-phenyl-2-butene has been prepared previously by addition of C$_6$H$_5$ and Cl units (generated by decomposition of C$_6$H$_5$N$_2$Cl in the presence of a catalytic amount of CuCl$_2$) across the conjugated system of butadiene, followed by treatment with ethanolic potassium iodide solution.[3]

The present preparation illustrates a general and convenient method for the *trans*-iodopropenylation of an alkyl halide.[4] The iodopropenylated material is not usually stable but is a useful synthetic intermediate. For example, it forms a stable crystalline triphenylphosphonium salt for use in the Wittig reaction, and under Kornblum reaction conditions (DMSO–NaHCO$_3$, 130°, 3 minutes) it gives an (*E*)-α,β-unsaturated aldehyde.[4] In addition to the phosphonium salt described in Note 15, the following have been prepared: (4-*p*-methoxyphenyl-2-butenyl)-triphenylphosphonium iodide [Phosphonium, [4-(4-methoxyphenyl)-2-butenyl]triphenyl-, iodide], m.p. 123–127°; (2-octenyl)triphenyl-phosphonium iodide [Phosphonium, 2-octenyltriphenyl-, iodide], m.p. 98°; and (2-octadecenyl)triphenylphosphonium iodide [Phosphonium, 2-octadecenyltriphenyl-, iodide], m.p. 50°.

The alkylation of 2-allylthio-2-thiazoline is noteworthy, since in general the coupling between an alkyllithium and an alkyl halide gives many by-products due to halogen–metal interconversion.[5] In the present case, alkylation α to sulfur occurred cleanly, which may be attributed to a five-membered chelating effect.[6] In some cases, addition of 1/10–1/20 volume of hexamethylphosphortriamide [Phosphoric triamide, hexamethyl-] to the tetrahydrofuran solution facilitates the alkylation [see *Org. Syn.*, **55**, 103 (1976) for a toxicity warning concerning this compound]. Representative alkyl halides examined and the yields of isolated products are as follows: (a) amyl bromide [Pentane, 1-bromo-] (63%), (b) decyl bromide [Decane, 1-bromo-] (70%), (c) anisyl chloride [Benzene, 1-(chloromethyl)-4-methoxy-] (57%), (d) phenethyl bromide [Benzene, (2-bromoethyl)-] (59%), and (e) cyclohexyl bromide [Cyclohexane, bromo-] (52%).[4,6a] The same type of alkylation occurred successfully with anions of 2-methylthio-2-thiazoline [Thiazole, 4,5-dihydro-2-(methylthio)-], 2-cinnamylthio-2-thiazoline [Thiazole, 4,5-dihydro-2-[(3-phenyl-2-propenyl)thio]-], and 2-benzylthio-2-thiazoline [Thiazole, 4,5-dihydro-2-[(phenylmethyl)thio]-], but attempts to alkylate 2-ethylthio-2-thiazoline [Thiazole, 2-(ethylthio)-4,5-dihydro-], 2-methylthio-2-benzothiazole [Benzothiazole, 2-(methylthio)-], or 2-allylthio-2-benzothiazole [Benzothiazole, 2-(2-propenylthio)-] were unsuccessful.

The final step, C—S bond cleavage with allylic rearrangement, incorporates two useful features. First, it is stereospecific, producing only the (E)-iodopropenylated product. Second, the sulfur-containing moiety is converted to a water-soluble product, and thus the desired material may be isolated in reasonable purity by a simple water–ether partitioning of the crude reaction mixture. The present procedure thus represents an improvement over a previous iodomethylation sequence (lithiation of thioanisole [Benzene, methylthio-], alkylation, and cleavage with methyl iodide and sodium iodide in dimethylformamide at 75°), in which the product must be separated from thioanisole.[7]

1. Central Research Laboratories, Sankyo Company Ltd., Tokyo 140.
2. B. Loev and M. M. Goodman, *Chem. Ind. London*, 2026 (1965).
3. A. V. Dombrovskĭi and A. P. Terent'ev, *Zh. Obshch. Khim.*, **26**, 2776 (1956) [*C.A.*, **51**, 7337*d* (1957)].
4. K. Hirai and Y. Kishida, *Tetrahedron Lett.*, 2743 (1972).
5. R. G. Jones and H. Gilman, *Org. React.*, **6**, 339 (1951).

6. (a) K. Hirai, H. Matsuda, and Y. Kishida, *Tetrahedron Lett.*, 4359 (1971); (b) T. Mukaiyama, K. Narasaka, K. Maekawa, and M. Furusato, *Bull. Chem. Soc. Jap.*, **44**, 2285 (1971).

7. E. J. Corey and M. Jautelat, *Tetrahedron Lett.*, 5787 (1968).

METHYL GROUPS BY REDUCTION OF AROMATIC CARBOXYLIC ACIDS WITH TRICHLOROSILANE–TRI-*n*-PROPYLAMINE: 2-METHYLBIPHENYL

[1,1'-Biphenyl, 2-methyl]

$$\underset{\text{CO}_2\text{H}}{\bigcirc\bigcirc} \xrightarrow[\substack{\text{2. (CH}_3\text{CH}_2\text{CH}_2)_3\text{N} \\ \text{reflux}}]{\substack{\text{1. SiHCl}_3 \\ \text{CH}_3\text{CN} \\ \text{reflux}}} \underset{\text{CH}_2\text{SiCl}_3}{\bigcirc\bigcirc} + \text{Chlorosiloxanes}$$

$$\underset{\text{CH}_2\text{SiCl}_3}{\bigcirc\bigcirc} \xrightarrow[\substack{\text{2. KOH} \\ \text{H}_2\text{O, CH}_3\text{OH} \\ \text{reflux}}]{\substack{\text{1. CH}_3\text{OH} \\ \text{reflux}}} \underset{\text{CH}_3}{\bigcirc\bigcirc} + \text{Siloxane Polymer}$$

Submitted by GEORGE S. LI, DAVID F. EHLER, and R. A. BENKESER[1]

Checked by KYO OKADA and WATARU NAGATA

1. Procedure

Caution! This procedure should be conducted in a well-ventilated hood to avoid inhalation of trichlorosilane and hydrogen chloride.

A 300-ml., three-necked, round-bottomed flask is equipped with a magnetic stirrer, a thermometer, a glass stopper, and an efficient condenser attached to a nitrogen line with a gas bubbler (Note 1). The system is flushed with dry nitrogen and then charged with 19.8 g. (0.10 mole) of 2-biphenylcarboxylic acid [[1,1'-Biphenyl]-2-carboxylic acid] (Note 2), 60 ml. (0.60 mole) of trichlorosilane [Silane, trichloro-] (Notes 3 and 4), and 80 ml. of acetonitrile (Note 5). A low nitrogen flow is maintained as the mixture is stirred and heated to reflux (40–45°) for 1 hour or until gas evolution ceases and the carboxylic acid has dissolved. The solution is then cooled in an acetone-dry ice bath to at least 0°, and the glass stopper is replaced with a 100-ml., pressure-equalizing dropping funnel charged with 37.8 g. (0.264 mole) of tri-n-propylamine [1-Propanamine, N,N-dipropyl-] (Notes 6 and 7), which is emptied rapidly into the stirred solution. The cooling bath is removed, and the flask contents are allowed to stir until the reaction ceases to be exothermic. A heating mantle is then used to maintain reflux for 16 hours (Note 8), during which time the temperature rises to 70–75°.

As soon as reflux is terminated, the solution is poured rapidly into a 1-l. Erlenmeyer flask, allowed to cool, and diluted with enough anhydrous ether (Note 9) to make a total volume of about 850 ml. (Note 10). After the flask has been sealed and refrigerated for one hour, the precipitate is removed by rapid filtration (water aspirator) through a 150-ml. Büchner funnel and washed with three 50-ml. portions of anhydrous ether. The clear yellow filtrate is concentrated as follows. A 300-ml., one-necked, round-bottomed flask is fitted with a magnetic stirring bar and a 100-mm. Vigreux column topped with a distillation head. The filtrate is placed in a 1-l., pressure-equalizing dropping funnel, which is inserted into the top of the distillation head. Approximately 100 ml. is run down through the column into the flask, which is then heated. As ether is removed by distillation, the remainder of the filtrate is dripped into the flask at a constant rate, and in this way the solution is concentrated into a small flask in a continuous operation. Distillation is continued until most of the ether has been removed, and the resulting murky solution is heated at 40° under a pressure of 80 mm. to remove the remaining volatiles.

The Vigreux column, dropping funnel, and distilling head are then replaced by a 100-ml., pressure-equalizing dropping funnel charged with 100 ml. of methanol. With the top of the funnel left open to the atmosphere, the methanol is added slowly to the oily flask contents (Note 11). After vigorous boiling has ceased, the solution is heated to reflux for one hour and then cooled in an ice bath and treated slowly with a solution of 56 g. (1.0 mole) of potassium hydroxide in 25 ml. of water and 50 ml. of methanol.[2] The resulting mixture is heated to reflux for 19 hours (Note 8), dissolved in 600 ml. of water, and extracted three times with 100 ml. of ether. The extracts are combined, washed once with 50 ml. of aqueous $5N$ hydrochloric acid, and dried over anhydrous magnesium sulfate. Ether is removed by distillation as described above, using a 300-ml., pressure-equalizing dropping funnel, a 50-ml., round-bottomed distilling flask, and a 100-mm. Vigreux column. Vacuum distillation of the remaining liquid gives 12.5–13.4 g. (74–80%) of 2-methylbiphenyl, b.p. 76–78° (0.5 mm.), n_D^{20} 1.5920 (Notes 12 and 13).

2. Notes

1. All glassware is thoroughly dried by flame or in an oven prior to use.

2. 2-Biphenylcarboxylic acid was purchased from Aldrich Chemical Company, Inc. and used without further purification.

3. The submitters used trichlorosilane supplied by Union Carbide Corporation. The checkers obtained trichlorosilane from Tokyo Chemical Industries Company, Ltd., Japan.

4. Good results may sometimes be achieved with a 4:1 or 5:1 mole ratio of trichlorosilane to carboxylic acid. Excess trichlorosilane is desirable to compensate for losses of this volatile reactant over extended reflux periods.

5. The submitters used reagent-grade acetonitrile (Mallinckrodt Chemical Works) dried prior to use by storage over Matheson Linde type 4A molecular sieves. The checkers used reagent-grade acetonitrile obtained from Ishizu Pharmaceutical Company, Japan, dried prior to use by storage over 4A molecular sieves obtained from Nakarai Chemicals, Ltd., Japan.

6. The submitters used tri-n-propylamine obtained from Aldrich Chemical Company, Inc., and the checkers used tri-n-propylamine obtained from Wako Pure Chemical Industries, Ltd., Japan. Both groups stored the reagent over Linde type 4A molecular sieves prior to use.

7. To ensure a homogeneous reducing medium, the tri-n-propyl-amine:trichlorosilane ratio should be about 1:2.

8. Overnight reflux was chosen partly for convenience. Similar results are possible with somewhat shorter reaction times.

9. The submitters employed anhydrous ether obtained from Mallinckrodt Chemical Works, and the checkers used anhydrous ether obtained from Wako Pure Chemical Industries, Ltd., Japan and distilled from sodium hydride under nitrogen shortly prior to use.

10. The volume of ether added should be sufficient to precipitate most of the tri-n-propylamine hydrochloride in solution. The checkers diluted to a total volume of about 1 l. to precipitate the salt more efficiently.

11. Vigorous evolution of hydrogen chloride is observed as the methanol is added.

12. The literature[3] value for a carefully purified sample of 2-methyl-biphenyl is n_D^{20} 1.5914.

13. Proton magnetic resonance ($CDCl_3$) δ, number of protons, multiplicity: 2.25 (3, singlet, CH_3), 7.27 (4, singlet, aryl CH), 7.33 (5, singlet, aryl CH); infrared ($CHCl_3$) cm.$^{-1}$: 1600 medium, 1480 medium strong (aromatic), 1380 medium (CH_3).

Gas chromatographic analysis of the product (1.5 m. by 0.5 cm. glass column, KF-54 on Chromosorb W, 60–80 mesh) showed a single peak with a retention time of 2.60 minutes at 170°.

3. Discussion

2-Methylbiphenyl has been prepared by diazotization of o-toluidine [Benzenamine, 2-methyl-] and coupling with benzene (8%);[4] by reaction of o-tolylmagnesium bromide [Magnesium, bromo(2-methyl-phenyl)-] with cyclohexanone, followed by dehydration of the resulting alcohol and dehydrogenation (30–50%);[5] and by coupling o-tolyllithium [Lithium, (2-methylphenyl)-] with chlorobenzene [Benzene, chloro-] in the presence of piperidine (51%).[6] The present procedure gives 2-methylbiphenyl in much improved yield.

In a more general sense, this reduction method provides a convenient pathway for converting an aromatic carboxyl group to a methyl group (see Table I).[7] Previously, this transformation has been achieved by reduction of the acid to the alcohol with lithium aluminum hydride, conversion of the alcohol to the tosylate, and a second reduction either with lithium aluminum hydride [Aluminate(1 −), tetrahydro, lithium,

TABLE I

Reduction of Aromatic Acids to Substituted Benzenes[7]

Starting Acid	Product (% Yield)
Benzoic	Toluene [Benzene, methyl-] (78)
m-Toluic [Benzoic acid, 3-methyl-]	m-Xylene [Benzene, 1,3-dimethyl-] (82)
p-Toluic [Benzoic acid, 4-methyl-]	p-Xylene [Benzene, 1,4-dimethyl-] (74)
3,5-Dimethylbenzoic [Benzoic acid, 3,5-dimethyl-]	Mesitylene [Benzene, 1,3,5-trimethyl-] (82)
p-Chlorobenzoic [Benzoic acid, 4-chloro-]	p-Chlorotoluene [Benzene, 1-chloro-4-methyl-] (94)
p-Bromobenzoic [Benzoic acid, 4-bromo-]	p-Bromotoluene [Benzene, 1-bromo-4-methyl-] (94)
Phthalic [1,2-Benzenedicarboxylic acid]	o-Xylene [Benzene, 1,2-dimethyl-] (64)

(T-4)-] or Raney nickel and hydrogen.[8] Alcohols of the benzylic type have also been reduced directly with hydrogen under pressure in the presence of various catalysts,[9] and benzoic acids have been reduced to toluenes with rhenium-type catalysts and hydrogen at high temperatures and pressures.[10]

1. Chemistry Department, Purdue University, West Lafayette, Indiana 47907.
2. C. Eaborn and S. H. Parker, *J. Chem. Soc. London*, 126 (1955). These authors note that similar cleavages have been effected in 4–8 hours with an excess of refluxing potassium hydroxide–methanol–water.
3. I. A. Goodman and P. H. Wise, *J. Amer. Chem. Soc.*, **72**, 3076 (1950).
4. M. Gomberg and J. C. Pernert, *J. Amer. Chem. Soc.*, **48**, 1372 (1926).
5. I. R. Sherwood, W. F. Short, and R. Stansfield, *J. Chem. Soc. London*, 1832 (1932). See also M. Orchin, *J. Amer. Chem. Soc.*, **67**, 499 (1945).
6. R. Huisgen, J. Sauer, and A. Hauser, *Chem. Ber.*, **91**, 2366 (1958).
7. R. A. Benkeser, K. M. Foley, J. M. Gaul, and G. S. Li, *J. Amer. Chem. Soc.*, **92**, 3232 (1970).
8. N. G. Gaylord, "Reduction with Complex Metal Hydrides," Interscience Publishers, Inc., New York, N.Y., 1956, p. 855.
9. R. L. Shriner and R. Adams, *J. Amer. Chem. Soc.*, **46**, 1683 (1924).
10. H. S. Broadbent, G. C. Campbell, W. J. Bartley, and J. H. Johnson, *J. Org. Chem.*, **24**, 1847 (1959); H. S. Broadbent and D. W. Seegmiller, *J. Org. Chem.*, **28**, 2347 (1963).

PEPTIDE SYNTHESES USING *N*-ETHYL-5-PHENYLISOXAZOLIUM-3′-SULFONATE: CARBOBENZOXY-L-ASPARAGINYL-L-LEUCINE METHYL ESTER AND *N*-CARBOBENZOXY-3-HYDROXY-L-PROLYLGLYCYLGLYCINE ETHYL ESTER

[L-Leucine, *N*-[*N²*-[(phenylmethoxy)carbonyl]-L-asparginyl]-, methyl ester and Glycine, *N*-[3-hydroxy-1-[(phenylmethoxy)-carbonyl]-L-prolyl]-, ethyl ester]

Submitted by R. B. Woodward and R. A. Olofson[1]
Checked by David L. Carroll, James C. Powers,
and Herbert O. House

1. Procedure

A. *Carbobenzoxy-L-asparaginyl-L-leucine Methyl Ester.* A mixture of 2.024 g. (0.0080 mole) of *N*-ethyl-5-phenylisoxazolium-3′-sulfonate [Isoxazolium, 2-ethyl-5-(3-sulfophenyl)-, hydroxide, inner salt] (Note 1) and 20 ml. of nitromethane (Note 2) is prepared in a 50-ml., glass-stoppered Erlenmeyer flask at room temperature and stirred vigorously with a magnetic stirrer (Note 3). A solution of 2.128 g. (0.0080 mole) of carbobenzoxy-L-asparagine [L-Asparagine, N^2-[(phenylmethoxy)carbonyl]-] (Note 4) and 810 mg. (0.0080 mole) of triethylamine (Notes 5 and 6) in 15 ml. of nitromethane (Note 2) is added, and stirring is continued until dissolution of the isoxazolium salt is practically complete to give a pale yellow solution (ca. 8 minutes is required; Note 3). Then 1.452 g. (0.0080 mole) of L-leucine methyl ester hydrochloride [L-Leucine, methyl ester, hydrochloride] (Note 7) is added, followed by a solution of 810 mg. (0.0080 mole) of triethylamine (Note 5) in 5 ml. of nitromethane (Note 2). The resulting mixture is stirred overnight at room temperature, during which time some solid may separate from the solution. The mixture is then transferred to a 100-ml., round-bottomed flask and concentrated under reduced pressure with a rotary evaporator. The residue is triturated with warm (ca. 60°) aqueous 0.5% sodium bicarbonate, and the resulting suspension is cooled and allowed to stand at 5° for at least 4 hours. The precipitate is collected on a filter, washed thoroughly with a total of 25 ml. of cold water, and dried to leave 2.36–2.65 g. (75–84%) of the crude peptide, which melts within the range of 168–178°. Recrystallization from an acetone–water mixture provides 2.09–2.21 g. (66–70%) of pure carbobenzoxy-L-asparaginyl-L-leucine methyl ester as fine, colorless crystals, m.p. 175–176.3°, $[\alpha]_D^{24}$ − 27.7° (c 1.0, methanol) (Note 8).

B. *N-Carbobenzoxy-3-hydroxy-L-prolylglycylglycine Ethyl Ester.* A mixture of 760 mg. (0.0030 mole) of N-ethyl-5-phenylisoxazolium-3′-sulfonate (Note 1) and 5 ml. of acetonitrile (Note 9) is prepared in a 25-ml., glass-stoppered Erlenmeyer flask. The mixture is cooled to 0° with an ice bath and stirred vigorously with a magnetic stirrer (Note 3). A solution of 796 mg. (0.0030 mole) of N-carbobenzoxy-3-hydroxy-L-proline [1,2-Pyrrolidinedicarboxylic acid, 3-hydroxy-, 1-(phenylmethyl) ester] (Note 10) and 304 mg. (0.0030 mole) of triethylamine (Notes 5 and 6) in 5 ml. of acetonitrile (Note 9) is added, and the cold (0–5°) mixture is stirred vigorously until almost all of the isoxazolium salt has dissolved (ca. 1–1.5 hours; Note 3). The cold (0–5°) reaction mixture is then treated with 590 mg. (0.0030 mole) of glycylglycine ethyl ester hydrochloride [Glycine, N-glycyl-, ethyl ester, monohydrochloride] (Note 11), followed by addition of a solution of 304 mg. (0.0030 mole) of triethylamine (Note 5) in 6 ml. of acetonitrile (Note 9). After this mixture has been stirred for 1 hour at 0–5°, the resulting pale yellow solution is allowed to warm to room temperature and is stirred overnight. The reaction solution is then transferred to a 100-ml., round-bottomed flask and concentrated under reduced pressure with a rotary evaporator. The residue is partitioned between 10 ml. of aqueous 1% sodium bicarbonate and 50 ml. of ethyl acetate. After the phases have been separated, the aqueous phase is extracted with three 10-ml. portions of ethyl acetate, and the combined organic extracts are dried over anhydrous sodium sulfate. The organic solution is concentrated under reduced pressure with a rotary evaporator, the residual white crystalline solid is triturated with 20 ml. of water, and the resulting slurry is cooled to 5° and allowed to stand overnight in a refrigerator. Filtration of the cold mixture provides a solid, which is washed with a small amount of cold water and dried. The combined aqueous filtrates are concentrated under reduced pressure with a rotary evaporator, and the residual solid is again triturated with 10 ml. of water, allowed to stand overnight at 5°, and filtered. The combined solids collected amount to 958–980 mg. (78–80%) of N-carbobenzoxy-3-hydroxy-L-prolylglycylglycine ethyl ester, m.p. 145–146°, $[\alpha]_D^{24}$ −18.5° (c 1.0, ethanol) (Note 12).

2. Notes

1. This isoxazolium salt (10 g.) (obtained from the Aldrich Chemical Company, Inc.) was dissolved in 45 ml. of aqueous 1 M hydrochloric acid and reprecipitated by the slow addition with swirling of 400 ml. of acetone. The salt was collected, washed with 300 ml. of acetone, and dried overnight at 25° under reduced pressure (< 1 mm.) to give a fluffy product, m.p. 206–208° (decomp.). An isomeric salt, N-ethyl-5-phenylisoxazolium-4′-sulfonate, which may be obtained by the usual synthetic procedure,[2] is also useful in peptide synthesis.

2. An anhydrous spectral grade of nitromethane, obtained from Fisher Scientific Company, was used without purification.

3. Since the initially formed enol ester rearranges slowly to an imide,[3] the yield depends on the rate at which the isoxazolium salt reacts, and that rate is increased by vigorous stirring. The reaction time for the activation step is approximately 8 minutes in nitromethane at 25° and approximately 1 hour in acetonitrile at 0°. In reactions performed with acetonitrile as the solvent, the checkers did not obtain complete solution. The reaction flask should be kept in a water bath to minimize heat transfer from the magnetic stirrer to the reaction mixture.

4. Carbobenzoxy-L-asparagine (obtained from the Aldrich Chemical

Company, Inc.) was recrystallized from an acetone–water mixture to give the pure acid, m.p. 162–163°.

5. Commercial triethylamine (obtained from Eastman Organic Chemicals), was distilled from phosphorus pentoxide, and the pure amine (b.p. 89–90°) was stored under a nitrogen atmosphere. Since the presence of even a small excess of triethylamine is deleterious in these reactions, the quantities of this amine used should be measured by weight rather than volume.

6. The triethylamine salts of peptide acids are often relatively insoluble in acetonitrile or nitromethane; therefore, the supersaturated solution formed on mixing the amine and the acid should be added to this reaction mixture immediately, before crystallization occurs. If crystallization does occur, the mixture should be heated to dissolve the salt, cooled rapidly, and added to the reaction mixture immediately. If it is impossible to obtain a solution of the salt, the peptide acid and then the triethylamine solution may be added separately to the reaction mixture with only a small sacrifice in yield.

7. L-Leucine methyl ester hydrochloride (obtained from the Mann Research Laboratories, Inc.) was recrystallized from a mixture of methanol and ether. The recrystallized salt melted at 149–150°.

8. The reported[4] rotation for this product is $[\alpha]_D^{23}$ $-26.3°$ (c 2.0, methanol). Infrared (KBr) cm.$^{-1}$: 3455, 3400, 3295 (amide NH stretching), 1737 (urethane and ester $C=O$), 1692 (amide $C=O$), 1647, 1535 (amide NH bending); proton magnetic resonance (DMSO-d_6) δ, number of protons, multiplicity, coupling constant J in Hz.: 8.17 (1, broad doublet, $J = 7$, NH), 7.35 (5, singlet, aromatic CH), 7.25 (2, broad, NH_2), 6.92 (1, broad, NH), 5.03 (2, singlet, benzylic CH_2), 4.1–4.7 (2, multiplet, $\diagdown$N—$\overset{|}{C}H$—CO—), 3.62 (3, singlet, OCH_3), 2.3–2.7 (2, multiplet, CH_2CO), 1.4–1.8 (3, multiplet, aliphatic CH), 0.7–1.1 (6, multiplet, CH_3); mass spectrum m/e (relative intensity): 393 (M^+, 1), 316 (5), 210 (12), 177 (15), 108 (37), 91 (100), 86 (50), 43 (28).

9. Reagent-grade acetonitrile (obtained from Eastman Organic Chemicals) was dried over Linde type 4A molecular sieves and then decanted and used without further purification.

10. N-Carbobenzoxy-3-hydroxy-L-proline (purchased from either Mann Research Laboratories or Sigma Chemical Company) was

recrystallized prior to use. The submitters recommend recrystallization from water, but the checkers found it easier to recrystallize the material from a mixture of ethyl acetate and petroleum ether (b.p. 30–60°). In either case, the checkers added a seed crystal to induce crystallization. The recrystallized product melted at 106–107°.

11. Glycylglycine ethyl ester hydrochloride (obtained from Nutritional Biochemicals Corporation) was recrystallized twice from mixtures of ethanol and ether to separate the pure salt, m.p. 181–182°.

12. The reported[5] rotation for this product (m.p. 144–145°) is $[\alpha]_D^{21}$ − 11.1° (c 1.0, ethanol). The submitters report that the melting point of the product is not changed by recrystallization. Infrared (CHCl$_3$) cm.$^{-1}$: 3390, 3295 (OH and NH stretching), 1730 (ester and urethane C=O), 1620 (broad, amide C=O), 1520 (broad, amide NH bending); proton magnetic resonance (CDCl$_3$) δ, number of protons, multiplicity, coupling constant J in Hz.: 7.6 (2, broad, NH), 7.30 (5, singlet, aromatic CH), 5.08 (2, singlet, benzylic CH_2), 3.5–4.7 (10, multiplet, OH and aliphatic CH), 2.0–2.4 (3, multiplet, aliphatic CH), 1.23 (3, triplet, J = 7, ethoxyl CH_3); mass spectrum, m/e (relative intensity): 207 (6), 149 (17), 108 (93), 107 (64), 91 (18), 79 (100), 77 (55), 65 (13).

3. Discussion

These procedures illustrate the use of N-ethyl-5-phenylisoxazolium-3′-sulfonate as a reagent for peptide synthesis.[2,3] Procedure A is recommended for peptides that are not soluble in either organic solvents or in water. Procedure B illustrates the formation of a peptide that is soluble both in organic solvents and in water. For peptides that are soluble in organic solvents and insoluble in water, the submitters recommend the use of Procedure B, except that the peptide product may be recovered directly from its solution in ethyl acetate after this organic solution has been washed successively with aqueous 5% sodium bicarbonate, water, aqueous 1 M hydrochloric acid, and water. Table I summarizes the preparation of various peptides by these procedures. Some more complex examples from other laboratories are listed elsewhere.[2b]

Since there are a number of excellent and extensive reviews of peptide chemistry,[6-9] no attempt will be made here to describe the known methods of peptide synthesis. Absolute comparisons of the procedure presented herein with other methods of peptide synthesis are impossible

TABLE I[2]

Peptide	Reaction Procedure	Yield
Z-(N^ε-Z)-Lys·Gly-OEt[Glycine, N-[N^2,N^6-bis-[(phenylmethoxy)carbonyl]-L-lysyl]-, ethyl ester]	B	95%
Z-Phe·Gly-OEt[Glycine, N-[N-[(phenylmethoxy)carbonyl]-L-phenylalanyl]-, ethyl ester]	B	93%
Z-Phe·Leu-OMe[L-Leucine, N-[N-[(phenylmethoxy)carbonyl]-L-phenylalanyl]-, methyl ester]	B	90%
Z-Met·Gly·Gly-OEt[Glycine, N-[N-[N-(phenylmethoxy)carbonyl]-L-methionyl]glycyl-, ethyl ester]	B	86%
Phth-Gly·Gly-OEt[Glycine, N-[(1,3-dihydro-1,3-dioxo-2H-isoindol-2-yl)acetyl]-, ethyl ester]	B	88%
Z-Gly·Gly·Tyr-OMe[L-Tyrosine, N-[N-[N-[(phenylmethoxy)carbonyl]glycyl]glycyl]-, methyl ester]	B	84%
Z-Gly·DL-Phe·Gly-OEt[Glycine, N-[N-[N-[(phenylmethoxy)carbonyl]glycyl]-DL-phenylalanyl]-, ethyl ester]	A	89%
Z-Gly·Gly·Gly-OEt[Glycine, N-[N-[N-[(phenylmethoxy)carbonyl]glycyl]glycyl]-, ethyl ester]	A	91%
Z-Gly-NHBz[Carbamic acid, [2-oxo-2-[(phenylmethyl)amino]ethyl]-, phenylmethyl ester]	A	94%
Z-Asp·Gly-OEt [Glycine, N-[N^2-[(phenylmethoxy)carbonyl]-L-asparaginyl]-, ethyl ester]	A	80%
Z-Gln·Val-OMe[L-Valine, N-[N^2-[(phenylmethoxy)carbonyl]-L-glutaminyl]-, methyl ester]	A	77%
Z-Gln·Tyr-OMe[L-Tyrosine, N-[N^2-[(phenylmethoxy)carbonyl]-L-glutaminyl]-, methyl ester]	A	75%

due to a number of factors: (a) the practice of many authors of reporting only yields of crude materials of unknown purity, (b) the necessities that prompt many experimenters to use a large excess of either the carboxyl component or the amine component in peptide synthesis, and (c) the difficulty of comparing this one-step synthesis of the amide bond with the ordinary two- and three-step syntheses (carboxyl activation, isolation of the free amine component from its hydrohalide, and aminolysis of the activated carboxyl group).

The method illustrated here does have, however, several excellent features.[10] The peptide yields are very good even in the synthesis of asparaginyl and glutaminyl peptides, which are ordinarily very difficult to prepare in reasonable yield. Furthermore, the by-products are all water-soluble and, therefore, easily removed from the product peptide derivative. One recrystallization, even under conditions of almost complete precipitation, usually suffices to yield pure material. A stringent test of this statement is the synthesis of carbobenzoxy-hydroxy-L-prolylglycylglycine ethyl ester, a peptide which is itself very soluble in water. The water solubility of the starting isoxazolium salt and of the by-products from coupling has also been useful in studies of the reaction of proteins with the isoxazolium salt in aqueous solution [11,12] and to effect intermolecular cross linking of polypeptides.[13] Finally, use of the isoxazolium salt procedure for activation of the carboxyl groups of serine, tyrosine, and threonine offers the advantage that protection of the hydroxyl groups is often unnecessary.[9b] Among the disadvantages of this method of peptide synthesis are the high cost of the isoxazolium salt and the limitations in the choice of solvent.

In tests devised to determine the amount of racemization to be expected in peptide syntheses in which the carboxyl component is a di- or higher peptide, this method ranks below the racemization-resistant azide procedure but above almost all other standard methods. Using a very sensitive and accurate isotope dilution assay, 1% racemization was observed [14] in the formation of the Anderson test peptide (Z-Gly-Phe-Gly-OEt) [15] and 7% racemization was observed [14] in the formation of the Young test peptide (Bz-Leu-Gly-OEt) [16] under optimized conditions. (The Young test was designed to exaggerate racemization problems, thus permitting more accurate studies of the effects of reaction condition variations.)

1. Department of Chemistry, Harvard University, Cambridge, Massachusetts 02138.
2. (a) R. B. Woodward, R. A. Olofson, and H. Mayer, *J. Amer. Chem. Soc.*, **83**, 1010 (1961); (b) R. B. Woodward, R. A. Olofson, and H. Mayer, *Tetrahedron*, **Suppl. 8**, Pt. I, 321 (1967).
3. R. B. Woodward and R. A. Olofson, *J. Amer. Chem. Soc.*, **83**, 1007 (1961); R. B. Woodward and R. A. Olofson, *Tetrahedron*, **Suppl. 7**, 415 (1966).
4. W. Koenig and R. Geiger, *Chem. Ber.*, **103**, 788 (1970).
5. N. C. Davis and E. L. Smith, *J. Biol. Chem.*, **200**, 373 (1953).
6. G. W. Kenner and M. Goodman, *Adv. Protein Chem.*, **12**, 465 (1957).
7. J. P. Greenstein and M. Winitz, "Chemistry of Amino Acids," John Wiley and Sons, Inc., New York, N.Y., 1961, p. 763.
8. E. Schröder and K. Lübke, "The Peptides," Vol. 1, Academic Press, Inc., New York, N.Y., 1965.
9. (a) M. Bodanszky and M. Ondetti, "Peptide Synthesis," John Wiley and Sons, Inc., New York, N.Y., 1966; (b) Y. S. Klausner and M. Bodanszky, *Synthesis*, 453 (1972).
10. In a survey of the methods used for peptide synthesis in 1968, the isoxazolium salt method was used in 7% of the examples surveyed: J. H. Jones in "Amino Acids, Peptides, and Proteins," Vol. 2, The Chemical Society, London, 1970, p. 145.
11. P. Bodlaender, G. Feinstein, and E. Shaw, *Biochemistry*, **8**, 4941 (1969).

12. G. Feinstein, P. Bodlaender, and E. Shaw, *Biochemistry*, **8**, 4949 (1969).
13. P. S. Marfey, T. J. Gill, and H. W. Kunz, *Biopolymers*, **3**, 27 (1965).
14. D. S. Kemp, S. W. Wang, G. Busby, and G. Hugel, *J. Amer. Chem. Soc.*, **92**, 1043 (1970).
15. G. W. Anderson and F. M. Callahan, *J. Amer. Chem. Soc.*, **80**, 2902 (1958).
16. M. W. Williams and G. T. Young, *J. Chem. Soc. London*, 881 (1963).

POLYMERIC CARBODIIMIDE. I. PREPARATION

[Benzene, diethenyl-, polymer with ethenylbenzene,
[[[[(1-methylethyl)imino]methylene]amino]methyl]deriv.]

$\widehat{P}$ = styrene–divinylbenzene copolymer

Submitted by NED M. WEINSHENKER, CHAH M. SHEN, and JACK Y. WONG[1]
Checked by A. FUKUZAWA and S. MASAMUNE

1. Procedure

A. *Polymeric Benzylamine* [*Benzene, diethenyl-, polymer with ethenylbenzene, aminomethylated*]. In a 300-ml., one-necked, round-bottomed flask equipped with a reflux condenser and a magnetic stirrer are placed

125 ml. of N,N-dimethylformamide (Note 1) and 10.00 g. of chloro-methylated polystyrene beads [Benzene, diethenyl-, polymer with ethenylbenzene, chloromethylated] (0.0106 mole of active chloride) (Notes 2 and 3). A gas inlet is attached to the top of the condenser, and the system is maintained under a slight positive pressure of nitrogen. The temperature is then raised to 100° by means of an oil bath, and 2.95 g. (0.0159 mole) of potassium phthalimide [1H-Isoindole-1,3-(2H)-dione, potassium salt] (Notes 4 and 5) is added while the mixture is stirred. After stirring at 100° overnight, the mixture is cooled and filtered. The polymer beads are washed with 200 ml. each of distilled water and methanol and then dried under reduced pressure to give 11.70 g. of phthalimido polymer.

The beads prepared above (11.58 g.) are suspended in 175 ml. of boiling absolute ethanol, and 0.94 g. (0.0159 mole) of aqueous 85% hydrazine monohydrate is added with stirring. The resulting mixture is refluxed for 10 hours, after which the polymer is collected by filtration and washed with 150-ml. portions of ethanol, aqueous 0.2N sodium hydroxide, distilled water, and anhydrous methanol. After vacuum drying at 60° for four hours, the yield of polymeric benzylamine is 10.38 g.

B. *Polymeric Urea* [*Benzene, diethenyl-, polymer with ethenylbenzene*, [[[[(1-*methylethyl*)*amino*]*carbonyl*]*amino*]*methyl*] *deriv.*] A 10.0-g. portion of benzylamine polymer beads prepared as in Part A and 125 ml. of tetrahydrofuran (Note 6) are combined in a 300-ml., three-necked, round-bottomed flask equipped with a magnetic stirrer, a dropping funnel, and a condenser fitted with a gas-inlet tube. A nitrogen atmos-phere is established in the system, and the slurry is stirred while 1.35 g. (0.0159 mole) of isopropyl isocyanate [Propane, 2-isocyanato-] is added. This causes an exothermic reaction, which subsides after about 20 minutes. The mixture is then stirred at room temperature for 22 hours and at reflux for an additional 4 hours. The beads are collected by filtration, washed with 150-ml. portions of tetrahydrofuran (Note 6) and methanol, and dried under reduced pressure over calcium chloride to yield 9.09 g. of the isopropyl urea polymer.

C. *Polymeric Carbodiimide.* The polymeric urea prepared above (9.09 g.) is combined with 100 ml. of dichloromethane in a 300-ml., three-necked, round-bottomed flask equipped with a magnetic stirrer, a condenser fitted with a gas-inlet tube, and a stopper. Under a blanket of nitrogen, 5.76 g. (0.057 mole) of triethylamine [Ethanamine, N,N-

diethyl-] and 2.75 g. (0.0145 mole) of 4-toluenesulfonyl chloride [Benzenesulfonyl chloride, 4-methyl-] (Note 7) are added to the stirred reaction mixture. The resulting slurry is refluxed with stirring for 50 hours, cooled to room temperature, and filtered. The polymer beads are washed successively with 100-ml. portions of dichloromethane, ice water, 3:1 dioxane–water, dioxane, and anhydrous ether. After vacuum drying, there is obtained 8.61 g. of polymeric carbodiimide containing 0.98–1.01 millimoles of carbodiimide per gram (Note 8).

2. Notes

1. N,N-Dimethylformamide was dried overnight over Linde type 4A molecular sieves.

2. The checkers used beads of chloromethylated polymer available from Bio. Rad. Laboratories, Richmond, California (Bio Beads S·X2). Chlorine analysis (Note 3) showed that the resin contained 1.06 milliequivalents of chlorine per gram, as specified by the manufacturer.

The submitters prepared the polymer as follows. *Caution! Chloromethyl methyl ether [Methane, chloromethoxy-] is a carcinogen and is listed as such on the OSHA list. Therefore, preparation of the chloromethylated resin must be performed in a fume hood, the operator must wear gloves, and the reagent must be disposed of in an appropriate manner.* A slurry of 200 g. (1.93 moles) of polystyrene crosslinked with 2% divinylbenzene [Benzene, diethenyl-, polymer with ethenylbenzene] (Amberlite XE-305, obtained from the Rohm and Haas Company, Philadelphia) and 2.5 l. of chloroform was prepared in a 3-l., three-necked, round-bottomed flask equipped with a dropping funnel, a condenser, and a mechanical stirrer. After stirring for 0.5 hour at room temperature, the mixture was cooled in an ice water bath, and a mixture of chloromethyl methyl ether (430 ml., 5.69 moles) and anhydrous stannic chloride [Stannane, tetrachloro-] (45 ml., 0.39 mole) was added dropwise with continuous stirring. After the addition was completed, the ice bath was removed, and the mixture was stirred for an additional 4 hours at room temperature. The beads were collected by filtration and washed successively with 2 l. of a 3:1 mixture of dioxane–water, 2 l. of a 3:1 mixture of dioxane–aqueous $3N$ hydrochloric acid, 1 l. of dioxane, 1 l. of water, and 1 l. of methanol. It is desirable to allow each of the solvents used in the washing procedure to be in contact with the beads for 5–10 minutes before filtration to ensure complete penetration. After drying over calcium chloride under reduced pressure, the chloromethylated polymer weighed 252 g. The chlorine content was 15.50%, equivalent to 4.29 milliequivalents of chlorine per gram of polymer (Note 3).

3. The chlorine content can be determined by either chlorine elemental analysis or a potentiometric titration using a chloride-ion electrode. For titration, about 0.2 g. of polymer is heated in 3 ml. of pyridine at 100° for 2 hours. This suspension is then transferred to a 50-ml. beaker containing 30 ml. of aqueous 50% acetic acid and 5 ml. of concentrated nitric acid, and the resulting mixture is titrated against aqueous 0.1N silver nitrate.

4. All chemicals used were reagent grade unless otherwise specified. A 50% molar excess of reagents was employed throughout the synthesis in order to drive the reactions to completion.

5. Potassium phthalimide was washed with acetone prior to use according to the procedure of Bornstein, Drummond, and Bedell.[2]

6. Tetrahydrofuran was dried and distilled from lithium aluminum hydride prior to use. For a warning concerning potential hazards of this procedure, see *Org. Syn.*, Coll. Vol. **5**, 976 (1973).

7. 4-Toluenesulfonyl chloride was recrystallized from hexane prior to use.

8. The *maximum* content of active carbodiimide groups can be determined by a nitrogen elemental analysis. The submitters determined the *minimum* carbodiimide content by treating the reagent with excess acetic acid: *ca.* 1 g. of accurately weighed polymeric carbodiimide was suspended in a mixture of 7 ml. of benzene, 3 ml. of ether, and 1.2 g. of acetic acid. After 20 hours of stirring, the conversion to acetic anhydride was determined by gas chromatography using a Carbowax 20M column operated at 160°. Triglyme [2,5,8,11-Tetraoxadodecane] was used as an internal standard. The final, deactivated polymer still showed a very strong absorption at 2140 cm.$^{-1}$ (KBr) in its infrared spectrum. The checkers modified the above procedure slightly by using glutaric acid [Pentanedioic acid] instead of acetic acid.

3. Discussion

The general procedure described here was originally published by the submitters,[3] who have used this insoluble reagent to prepare aldehydes and ketones under Moffat oxidation conditions.[4] A polymeric reagent offers two advantages: (a) when an oxidation is complete, the urea by-product is cleanly separated from products by a simple filtration; and (b) the deactivated urea form of the polymer can be recycled efficiently to the carbodiimide form, as outlined in Part C of the present procedure. The use of polyhexamethylenecarbodiimide in peptide syntheses has been mentioned previously.[5]

1. Dynapol, 1454 Page Mill Road, Palo Alto, California 94304.
2. J. Bornstein, P. E. Drummond, and S. F. Bedell, *Org. Syn.*, Coll. Vol. **4**, 810 (1963).
3. N. M. Weinshenker and C. M. Shen, *Tetrahedron Lett.*, 3281 (1972).
4. N. M. Weinshenker and C. M. Shen, *Tetrahedron Lett.*, 3285 (1972); N. M. Weinshenker, C. M. Shen, and J. Y. Wong, *Org. Syn.*, **56**, 99.
5. Y. Wolman, S. Kivity, and M. Frankel, *Chem. Commun.*, 629 (1967).

POLYMERIC CARBODIIMIDE. II. MOFFAT OXIDATION:
4-*tert*-BUTYLCYCLOHEXANONE

[Cyclohexanone, 4-(1,1-dimethylethyl)-]

(P) = styrene–divinylbenzene copolymer

Submitted by NED M. WEINSHENKER, CHAH M. SHEN, and JACK Y. WONG[1]
Checked by A. FUKUZAWA and S. MASAMUNE

1. Procedure

In a 250-ml., three-necked, round-bottomed flask equipped with a mechanical stirrer, a gas inlet, and a stopper are placed 540 mg. (0.00346 mole) of a mixture of *cis*- and *trans*-4-*tert*-butylcyclohexanols [Cyclohexanol, 4-(1,1-dimethylethyl)-, *cis*- and *trans*-] (Note 1), 50 ml. of anhydrous benzene (Note 2), and 25 ml. of anhydrous dimethyl sulfoxide (Note 3). While a slight positive pressure of argon is maintained in the system, 13.19 g. of carbodiimide resin [Benzene, diethenyl-, polymer with ethenylbenzene, [[[[(1-methylethyl)imino]methylene]-amino]methyl] deriv.] (Note 4) is added, followed by 0.2 ml. of dimethyl sulfoxide (Note 3) containing 98 mg. (0.0010 mole) of anhydrous ortho-phosphoric acid (Note 5). The resulting mixture is stirred at room temperature for 3.5 days. The beads are then separated by filtration and washed with three 100-ml. portions of ether, and the combined filtrates are washed with five 100-ml. portions of water. After evaporation of the organic phase to dryness, the residue crystallizes to provide 446–450 mg. (83–84%) of crude 4-*tert*-butylcyclohexanone, m.p. 42–45° (Note 6). The deactivated carbodiimide resin can be regenerated by treatment with triethylamine [Ethanamine, *N,N*-diethyl-] and 4-toluenesulfonyl chloride [Benzenesulfonyl chloride, 4-methyl-] (Note 4).

2. Notes

1. This mixture is available from Aldrich Chemical Company, Inc. The checkers used a 7:93 mixture of the *cis*- and *trans*-isomers, prepared by lithium aluminum hydride [Aluminate(1 −), tetrahydro-, lithium, (*T*-4)-] reduction of 4-*tert*-butylcyclohexanone and recrystallization of the crude product. The ketone was purchased from Aldrich Chemical Company, Inc.

2. Benzene was dried by distillation from sodium.

3. The submitters dried dimethyl sulfoxide using Linde type 3A molecular sieves. The checkers distilled this reagent from calcium hydride at 10 mm. prior to use.

4. The amount of resin used contains about 0.012 mole of active carbodiimide. Methods for preparing this reagent, determining its carbodiimide content, and regenerating spent resin are described in the preceeding procedure (p. 95).

5. Anhydrous orthophosphoric acid was prepared according to the equation:

$$P_2O_5 + 3H_2O \rightarrow 2H_3PO_4$$

The submitters added 5.88 ml. of aqueous 85% phosphoric acid to 3.98 g. of phosphorous pentoxide and heated the mixture for 15 minutes or until all of the solid had dissolved. The checkers placed 71.0 g. of phosphorous pentoxide in a flask, cooled it in ice, and cautiously added 27 ml. of water.

6. Infrared (CHCl$_3$) cm.$^{-1}$: 1712 (C=O). Gas chromatographic analysis (10% Carbowax 20M, 3 mm. by 1.8 m., 180°) showed the crude product to be 97% pure. 4-*tert*-Butylcyclohexanone has been reported to melt at 49.5–51°.[2]

3. Discussion

The general procedure described here was originally published by the submitters.[3] Both ketones and aldehydes may be prepared, and this method is particularly effective when the mild conditions of the Moffat oxidation are required, but the dicyclohexylurea by-product formed with the usual reagents causes purification problems.

1. Dynapol, 1454 Page Mill Road, Palo Alto, California 94304.
2. E. L. Eliel and M. N. Rerick, *J. Amer. Chem. Soc.*, **82**, 1367 (1960).
3. N. M. Weinshenker and C. M. Shen, *Tetrahedron Lett.*, 3285 (1972).

REDUCTIVE CLEAVAGE OF ALLYLIC ALCOHOLS, ETHERS, OR ACETATES TO OLEFINS: 3-METHYLCYCLOHEXENE

[Cyclohexene, 3-methyl-]

Submitted by I. ELPHIMOFF-FELKIN and P. SARDA[1]
Checked by M. L. LEE and G. BÜCHI

1. Procedure

A. *3-Methyl-2-cyclohexen-1-ol* [*2-Cyclohexen-1-ol, 3-methyl-*]. A solution of 33.6 g. (0.305 mole) of 3-methyl-2-cyclohexen-1-one [2-Cyclohexen-1-one, 3-methyl-] (Note 1) in 600 ml. of anhydrous ether is placed in a 2-l., three-necked, round-bottomed flask fitted with a mechanical stirrer, a reflux condenser attached to a source of dry nitrogen, and a pressure-equalizing dropping funnel. The solution is stirred and cooled in an ice bath while 471 ml. (0.0825 mole) of a 0.175 M solution of lithium aluminum hydride [Aluminate(1−), tetrahydro-, lithium, (T-4)-] in ether (Note 2) is added dropwise. When the addition is complete the reaction mixture is stirred at 0° for another 15 minutes, and then cooling and gentle stirring are continued while moist ether is added through the dropping funnel until gas is no longer evolved. The resulting slurry is then filtered, and the ethereal filtrate is washed with saturated aqueous sodium chloride and dried over magnesium sulfate. Removal of ether on a water bath and distillation of the residue under reduced pressure provides 33.7 g. (98%) of 3-methyl-2-cyclohexen-1-ol, b.p. 94–95° (31 mm.).

B. *Amalgamated Zinc [Mercury alloy (Hg, Zn)].* Zinc powder (206 g., 3.15 moles) is placed in a 1-l. beaker, covered with 250 ml. of aqueous 10% hydrochloric acid, and stirred for 2 minutes. The acid is then decanted and replaced by distilled water, the mixture is stirred, and the supernatant is decanted. Washing is continued in this way until the water is neutral to litmus. A warm solution of 40 g. (0.15 mole) of mercuric chloride [Mercury chloride (HgCl₂)] in 250 ml. of distilled water is then poured onto the zinc, and the mixture is stirred gently for 10 minutes. After filtration, the powder is washed with 250 ml. of distilled water, five 250-ml. portions of 95% ethanol, and five 250-ml. portions of anhydrous ether. Drying under vacuum gives 196 g. of zinc amalgam.

C. *3-Methylcyclohexene.* A 1-l., round-bottomed, three-necked flask equipped with a mechanical stirrer, a reflux condenser connected to a source of dry nitrogen, and a pressure-equalizing addition funnel is charged with 196 g. (3 moles) of dry amalgamated zinc powder (Note 3), 22.4 g. (0.20 mole) of 3-methyl-2-cyclohexen-1-ol, and 280 ml. of anhydrous ether. The flask is placed in an ethanol–water—dry ice bath, maintained at −15° throughout the reaction. The reaction mixture is stirred gently for 5 minutes and then stirred vigorously while 153 ml. (0.40 mole) of 2.6 M hydrogen chloride in anhydrous ether (Note 4) is added dropwise over 1.5 hours. When the addition is complete, stirring is continued for an additional 15 minutes, after which the reaction medium is neutral to moist litmus (Note 5).

Decanting the reaction mixture separates residual zinc, which is washed thoroughly with two 200-ml. portions of ether. The ethereal solutions are combined, washed sequentially with two 50-ml. portions of water, 50 ml. of aqueous 10% sodium bicarbonate, and two 50-ml. portions of saturated aqueous sodium chloride (Note 6), and finally dried over magnesium sulfate. After filtration to remove the drying agent, ether is removed by careful distillation through a Dufton column at atmospheric pressure (Note 7). When the residual solution is approximately 100 ml. in volume, it is transferred to a smaller apparatus and distilled slowly at atmospheric pressure. After a forerun of ether, 13.2–14.4 g. (68–75%) of 3-methylcyclohexene distils between 103° and 104° (Note 8).

2. Notes

1. The unsaturated ketone[2] can be purchased from Ega Chemie K.G. or from Frinton Laboratories, P.O. Box 301, South Vineland, New Jersey.

2. The concentration of this solution was established by decomposing the lithium aluminum hydride with excess iodine according to the following equation:

$$\text{LiAlH}_4 + 2\text{I}_2 \rightarrow 2\text{H}_2 + \text{LiI} + \text{AlI}_3$$

The amount of unreacted iodine was determined by titration with sodium thiosulfate [Thiosulfuric acid ($H_2S_2O_3$), disodium salt], and the amount of iodine initially present was determined by a separate blank titration.[3]

Working solutions were prepared by dissolving 40 g. of iodine in 1 l. of anhydrous benzene and by dissolving 248 g. of sodium thiosulfate pentahydrate in 1 l. of water (*ca.* 1 M); an accurately prepared 0.100N aqueous sodium thiosulfate solution is also required. For titration, a 25.0-ml. portion of the iodine solution was stirred vigorously in a 500-ml. Erlenmeyer flask, and 1.00 ml. of the lithium aluminum hydride solution was added rapidly, followed by 20 ml. of water, 2 drops of acetic acid, and 5.00 ml. of the 1 M sodium thiosulfate solution. With continued stirring, the solution was titrated to the colorless end point by adding V_a ml. of the 0.100N sodium thiosulfate solution.

Separately, another 25.0-ml. portion of the iodine solution was stirred in a 500-ml. Erlenmeyer flask and treated with 5.00 ml. of the 1 M aqueous sodium thiosulfate, 20 ml. of water, and 2 drops of acetic acid.

Titration was continued to the end point by adding, with continuous stirring, V_b ml. of 0.100N aqueous sodium thiosulfate. The molarity of the lithium aluminum hydride solution was then calculated from the following equation:

$$M = 0.025(V_b - V_a)$$

3. A large excess of zinc is used to make the reaction faster and to reduce the formation of polymeric by-products.

4. The solution of dry hydrogen chloride in ether was prepared as follows. Commercial hydrogen chloride gas was dried by passing it through an empty safety trap, a wash bottle of concentrated sulfuric acid, a calcium chloride tube, and another empty safety trap. Anhydrous ether was cooled in an ice bath, and the hydrogen chloride was bubbled through rapidly. Gas uptake was followed by weighing the ethereal solution occasionally, and the concentration of the final solution was determined by alcalimetric titration. The optimum concentration of hydrogen chloride is 2.5–3 M. Use of excess acid led to overreduction in the case of 2-phenyl-2-cyclohexen-1-ol, the desired 1-phenylcyclohexene being contaminated by some phenylcyclohexane.

5. If the total reaction time is less than approximately 1.75 hours, starting material remains. Therefore, if the ethereal hydrogen chloride is added in less than 1.5 hours, the subsequent stirring must be lengthened accordingly.

6. If zinc chloride is not removed by washing, it causes polymerization of the olefin during distillation.

7. Slow distillation of the ether is essential in order to prevent the low-boiling olefin from codistilling with the solvent. For higher-boiling olefins the ether can be removed on a water bath prior to distillation of the olefin under reduced pressure.

8. Gas chromatographic analysis, using an HMDS-treated Chromosorb W column with 7% Craig polyester as the stationary phase, indicated the product to have a purity of 97%. The 3% impurity is most probably the isomeric 1-methylcyclohexene.

3. Discussion

The model procedure described above is applicable to allylic alcohols, ethers, and acetates. The submitters' results for the conversion of several such compounds to the corresponding olefins, performed on a smaller scale, are summarized in Table I. Reductive cleavage of allylic alcohols, ethers, and acetates has often been reported in the literature. Typical reagents used are sodium in liquid ammonia,[4,5] zinc and acetic acid,[6] chloroaluminum hydride,[7] and propylmagnesium bromide [Magnesium, bromopropyl-] in the presence of dichlorobis(triphenylphosphine)nickel [Nickel, dichlorobis(triphenylphosphine)-].[8] In all of these procedures, however, when two or more isomeric olefins can be formed, the thermo-dynamically more stable olefin generally predominates. The advantage of the present procedure[9] is that it leads, depending on the structure of the starting material, either exclusively or predominantly to the less stable isomer (see Table I). These results have been interpreted[9] by assuming that reduction takes place through an intermediate that behaves like an allylic metal halide. Studies of allylic metal halides such as crotyl zinc halides[10] and the crotyl Grignard reagent[11] suggest that such an intermediate would be protonated predominantly at the more substituted end of the allylic system.

TABLE I

Olefins from Allylic Alcohols, Ethers, and Acetates[9]

Starting Material	Total yield of Olefins (%)[a]	Major Olefin (relative %)[b]	
	85–90		70
	85–90		70
	85–90		70
	85–90		70
	70		80

TABLE I (*Cont.*)

Starting Material	Total yield of Olefin (%)[a]	Major Olefin (relative %)[b]
OH, C_6H_5	80	C_6H_5	80
OH, CH_3	not determined	CH_3	80
CH_3, OH, H (*cis + trans*)[c]	70	CH_3, H	(racemic)
CH_3, $OCOCH_3$, H	70	CH_3, H	(racemic)
C_6H_5, $OCOCH_3$	80	C_6H_5	

[a] Distilled product.
[b] Determined by glc.
[c] From lithium aluminum hydride reduction of (−)carvone.

1. Institut de Chimie des Substances Naturelles, C.N.R.S., 91190 Gif-sur-Yvette, France.
2. M. W. Cronyn and G. H. Riesser, *J. Amer. Chem. Soc.*, **75**, 1664 (1953).
3. H. Felkin, *Bull. Soc. Chim. Fr.*, 347 (1951).
4. A. J. Birch, *Quart. Rev. Chem. Soc.*, **84**, 69 (1950).
5. A. S. Hallsworth, H. B. Henbest, and T. I. Wrigley, *J. Chem. Soc. London*, 1969 (1957).

6. L. F. Fieser and M. Fieser, "Steroids," Reinhold Publishing Corporation, Inc., New York, N.Y., 1959, p. 204.
7. J. H. Brewster and H. O. Bayer, *J. Org. Chem.*, **29**, 116 (1964).
8. H. Felkin and G. Swierczewski, *C.R.H. Acad. Sci. Ser. C*, **266**, 1611 (1968).
9. I. Elphimoff-Felkin and P. Sarda, *Tetrahedron Lett.*, 725 (1972).
10. R. Gaudemar, *Bull. Soc. Chim. Fr.*, 1475 (1958); *Bull. Soc. Chim. Fr.*, 974 (1962); C. Agami, M. Andrac-Taussig, and C. Prevost, *Bull. Soc. Chim. Fr.*, 1915, 2596 (1966).
11. R. A. Benkeser, *Synthesis*, 347 (1971).

RING CONTRACTION *via* A FAVORSKII-TYPE REARRANGEMENT: CYCLOUNDECANONE

Submitted by J. WOHLLEBE and E. W. GARBISCH, JR.[1]
Checked by J. M. DIAKUR and S. MASAMUNE

1. Procedure

Caution! Hydrazoic acid, which is used in Part C of this procedure, is very toxic. Consequently, the conversion of methyl cycloundec-1-enecarboxylate to cycloundecanone by the Schmidt degradation, including hydrolysis and subsequent steam distillation, should be conducted in a well-ventilated hood.

Pure hydrazoic acid in a condensed state has been reported in several instances to explode violently without apparent inducement, but explosions during Schmidt reactions do not seem to have been observed. Nevertheless, it is recommended that this reaction be carried out behind a safety shield.

A. 2,12-*Dibromocyclododecanone* [*Cyclododecanone, 2,12-dibromo-*]. A

3-l., three-necked, round-bottomed flask is fitted with magnetic stirring (Note 1), a pressure-equalizing dropping funnel, a thermometer, and a gas-outlet tube. The outlet tube is connected by Tygon tubing to a calcium chloride drying tube, which is placed near an exhaust port of a hood. The flask is charged with 182 g. (1.00 mole) of cyclododecanone (Note 2), 1.4 l. of dry benzene (Note 3), and 150 ml. of anhydrous ether, and the funnel is charged with 320 g. (2.0 moles) of bromine (Note 4). The reaction vessel is then immersed in a water bath, stirring is initiated, and bromine is added at such a rate that the bromine in solution is consumed before the addition of each new drop; the addition requires 20–30 minutes. Ice is added to the water bath as required to hold the reaction temperature at 20–25°. The gas-outlet tube is then connected to a water aspirator, the dropping funnel is replaced by a stopper, and the water bath is filled with warm water. While stirring is continued, the pressure in the reaction flask is gradually decreased to evaporate the hydrobromic acid formed (together with most of the ether and some of the benzene) until the aspirator water is neutral to indicator paper (Note 5). Approximately 1 l. of solution remains in the flask, and this is used directly for the next step.

B. *Methyl Cycloundec-1-enecarboxylate* [1-*Cycloundecene-1-carboxylic acid, methyl ester*]. The benzene solution of 2,12-dibromocyclododecanone prepared in Part A is stirred and treated with 125 g. (2.31 moles) of powdered sodium methoxide [Methanol, sodium salt] (Note 6), which is added in portions during 30–40 minutes. Ice is added to the water bath as required to hold the reaction temperature at 25–30°. After being stirred at 25–30° for another 20 minutes, the reaction mixture is extracted successively with 500-ml. portions of water, aqueous 5% hydrochloric acid, and saturated aqueous sodium chloride. The aqueous phases are combined, extracted with 400 ml. of ether, and discarded. The combined organic phases are filtered through anhydrous sodium sulfate, the solvents are evaporated under reduced pressure, and the residual oil is distilled through a 7-cm. insulated Vigreux column under a pressure of 0.4 mm. Collection of the fractions boiling below 104° provides 191–196 g. (91–93%) of methyl cycloundec-1-enecarboxylate (Note 7) as a pale yellow oil, most of which distils at 83–87° (0.4 mm.). This ester is sufficiently pure for use in the next step.

C. *Cycloundecanone.* In a well-ventilated hood a 3-l., three-necked, round-bottomed flask is fitted with a magnetic stirrer (Note 1), a thermometer, a reflux condenser protected by a calcium chloride tube, and a rubber stopper. Concentrated sulfuric acid (600 ml.) is placed in the flask, stirred slowly, and cooled to 5° with an ice bath. The methyl cycloundec-1-enecarboxylate prepared in Part B (191–196 g., 0.91–0.92 mole) is added through a long-stemmed funnel, the rate of stirring is increased until the mixture becomes a homogeneous solution, and then 500 ml. of chloroform is added. The resulting mixture is heated to 35° by immersion in a bath of warm water. Vigorous stirring is continued while 78 g. (1.2 moles) of sodium azide (Note 8) is added in small portions over a 30–50-minute period, the reaction temperature being maintained at 40 ± 2° by adding ice to the water bath. *Caution! This operation should be performed behind a safety shield.* After an additional 10–15 minutes of stirring at 35–40°, the reaction mixture is cooled to 5°, poured onto 1 kg. of ice, and transferred together with 1.5–2 l. of water to a 5-l., three-necked flask set up for steam distillation. The chloroform is distilled off and saved, and then the cycloundecanone is steam distilled with 3.5–4.0 kg. of steam. The steam distillate is extracted with the recovered chloroform, then with 500 ml. of diethyl ether. After the ethereal extract has been washed with concentrated aqueous sodium chloride, the organic phases are filtered through anhydrous sodium sulfate, combined, and concentrated under reduced pressure. Vacuum distillation of the residual oil affords 139–143 g. (83–85%) of cycloundecanone as a colorless or pale yellow oil, b.p. 84–85° (2 mm.), n_D^{25} 1.4794–1.4796 (Note 8).

2. Notes

1. A Thomas Magne-Matic Stirrer Model 15 (available from the Arthur H. Thomas Company, Philadelphia) was used in conjunction with a 5-cm., Teflon-coated, egg-shaped magnet.

2. Cyclododecanone was obtained from Aldrich Chemical Company, Inc. and used without purification.

3. Solvent-grade benzene was dried over sodium wire prior to use. If a voluminous sludge forms on drying, the solvent should be distilled from sodium.

4. Various brands and grades of bromine were used without noticeable difference (however, *cf.* reference 6). Bromine was added until a light orange color persisted for more than 2 minutes, which occasionally required the addition of a few drops in excess of the theoretical amount.

5. At this stage, the addition of a small amount of anhydrous

potassium bicarbonate powder to the residual reaction mixture should not cause evolution of carbon dioxide gas.

6. The submitters used the reagent as supplied by Mallinckrodt Chemical Works. The checkers have occasionally found that commercially available sodium methoxide has deteriorated on storage over an extended period, unless the reagent has been properly protected from moisture. Therefore, it was prepared in the following manner. A 2-l., three-necked, round-bottomed flask was equipped with a magnetic stirrer and a reflux condenser and flushed with dry nitrogen through a gas bubbler attached to the top of the condenser. Into this flask was distilled approximately 600 ml. of absolute methanol (dried with magnesium methoxide), and then 69 g. of sodium was added in 1–3-g. portions. After all of the sodium had dissolved, the methanol was distilled, first at atmospheric and then at reduced pressure. The resulting mass of sodium methoxide was powdered under nitrogen and dried under vacuum at 150° for 8 hours. Titration of the reagent against $0.1311N$ aqueous hydrochloric acid showed it to be 97.5% pure.

7. Gas chromatographic analysis of the product showed two major peaks (relative intensity, 5:1), and the mass spectrum of each peak revealed a molecular ion at m/e 210. The proton magnetic resonance spectrum of the mixture showed that the two products were geometrically isomeric esters.

8. Sodium azide of practical grade was obtained from Eastman Organic Chemicals, and lumps were broken up with a spatula. Care was taken to avoid contact of sodium azide with the skin.

9. The cycloundecanone solidified on cooling and melted at 16.2–16.6°. Gas chromatographic analysis of the product showed a single peak [1.5 m. by 3.2 mm. column, 5% SE-30 on Chromosorb W, at 125° (submitters); 1.5 m. by 3.2 mm. column, UC-W98, 150°, retention time 10.25 minutes (checkers)]. Proton magnetic resonance ($CDCl_3$) δ, number of protons: 1.3–2.1 (16, multiplet), 2.4–2.7 (4, multiplet); infrared (neat) cm.$^{-1}$: 1700 very strong.

3. Discussion

Cycloundecanone has been prepared in several ways: (a) pyrolysis of the thorium salt of dodecanedioic acid [Dodecanedioic acid, thorium $(4+)$salt$(2:1)$],[2] (b) reduction of 2-hydroxycycloundecanone [Cycloundecanone, 2-hydroxy-],[3,4] (c) ring expansion of several lower homologs of cycloundecanone,[5] (d) Curtius degradation of cycloundec-1-enecarboxylic acid [1-Cycloundecene-1-carboxylic acid],[6] and (e) hydrolysis of 1-methoxycycloundecene [Cycloundecene, 1-methoxy-].[7]

The present method, a modification of a procedure described previously by the submitters,[8] gives higher yields and is less expensive and more expeditious than the previously published methods. This route, involving a Favorskii-type rearrangement, has the potential of being widely applicable for the preparation of the lower homolog of a ketone having at least one hydrogen atom at each α-position. For example, cyclodecanone has been prepared in 77% yield from cycloundecanone by essentially the same procedure.[8]

1. Department of Chemistry, University of Minnesota, Minneapolis, Minnesota 55455.
2. L. Ruzicka, M. Stoll, and H. Schinz, *Helv. Chim. Acta*, **9**, 249 (1926).
3. K. Ziegler, H. Sauer, L. Bruns, H. Froitzheim-Kühlhorn, and J. Schneider, *Justus Liebigs Ann. Chem.*, **589**, 122 (1954).
4. R. W. Fawcett and J. O. Harris, *J. Chem. Soc. London*, 2673 (1954).
5. E. Müller and M. Bauer, *Justus Liebigs Ann. Chem.*, **654**, 92 (1962).
6. K. Schank and B. Eistert, *Chem. Ber.*, **98**, 650 (1965).
7. Rhone-Poulenc S.A., Netherlands Patent 6,605,908 [*C.A.*, **66**, 85538*s* (1967)].
8. E. W. Garbisch, Jr. and J. Wohllebe, *J. Org. Chem.*, **33**, 2157 (1968).

SELECTIVE EPOXIDATION OF TERMINAL DOUBLE BONDS: 10,11-EPOXYFARNESYL ACETATE

[2,6-Nonadien-1-ol, 9-(3,3,-dimethyloxiranyl)-3,7-dimethyl-, acetate, (*E,E*)-]

Submitted by R. P. HANZLIK[1]
Checked by A. GRIEDER and G. BÜCHI

1. Procedure

A. *Farnesyl Acetate* [*2,6,10-Dodecatrien-1-ol, 3,7,11-trimethyl-, acetate, (E,E)-*]. A solution of 25 g. (0.11 mole) of farnesol [2,6,10-

Dodecatrien-1-ol, 3,7,11-trimethyl-, (E,E)-] (Note 1) and 40 ml. of dry pyridine (Note 2) is prepared in a stoppered 250-ml. Erlenmeyer flask, and 40 ml. of acetic anhydride is added in four portions over a 15-minute period. The mixture is stirred well and allowed to stand for 6 hours and then poured onto 250 g. of ice. Water is added (400 ml.), and the mixture is extracted with five 100-ml. portions of petroleum ether (b.p. 60–68°). The organic extracts are combined and washed in succession with two 50-ml. portions each of water, 5% aqueous sulfuric acid, and saturated aqueous sodium bicarbonate. Anhydrous magnesium sulfate (*ca.* 50 g.) is used to dry the petroleum ether solution, which is then concentrated on a rotary evaporator to provide 28–29 g. (94–98%) of farnesyl acetate as a colorless oil (Note 3).

B. 10-*Bromo*-11-*hydroxy*-10,11-*dihydrofarnesyl Acetate* [2,6-*Dodeca-diene*-1,11-*diol*, 10-*bromo*-3,7,11-*trimethyl*-, 1-*acetate*, (E,E)-]. Farnesyl acetate (29 g., 0.11 mole) is dissolved in 1 l. of *tert*-butyl alcohol (Note 4) contained in a 3-l. Erlenmeyer flask. Water is added (500 ml.), and the solution is cooled to about 12° using an external ice water bath. Maintaining this temperature, rapid magnetic stirring is begun, and more water is added until a saturated solution is obtained. The second addition of water may be rapid initially, but the saturation point must be approached carefully, like the end point of a titration. A total of about 1200 ml. of water is required for the above amounts of farnesyl acetate and *tert*-butyl alcohol. The solution must remain clear and homogeneous at about 12°, and if the saturation point is accidentally passed by adding too much water, *tert*-butyl alcohol should be added to remove the turbidity.

External cooling is now discontinued, and 21.4 g. (0.12 mole) of N-bromosuccinimide [2,5-Pyrrolidinedione, 1-bromo-] (Note 5) is added. Stirring is continued until all of the solid is dissolved (*ca.* 1 hour). The resulting solution, which may be pale yellow, is concentrated with a rotary evaporator (bath temperature 40–45°) to a volume of about 300 ml. and extracted with five 120-ml. portions of ether. The combined ether extracts are dried over anhydrous magnesium sulfate (20–50 g.), and removal of solvent at reduced pressure provides an oil, which is purified by column chromatography on silica gel (Note 6). Pure bromo-hydrin acetate is obtained as a colorless oil in amounts of up to 26 g., a 65% yield based on farnesyl acetate (Notes 7 and 8).

C. 10,11-*Epoxyfarnesyl Acetate.* The bromohydrin acetate prepared in Part B is dissolved in 300 ml. of methanol, the solution is placed in a

500-ml. flask, and excess solid potassium carbonate (three times the molar amount of bromohydrin acetate) is added (Note 9). The mixture is stirred for 12 hours and then concentrated to *ca.* 100 ml. on a rotary evaporator (bath at 40–45°). Water is added (200 ml.), and the mixture is extracted with four 100-ml. portions of petroleum ether (b.p. 60–68°). The combined extracts are dried over anhydrous magnesium sulfate (*ca.* 40 g.) and evaporated, leaving behind 10,11-epoxyfarnesol [2,6-Dodecadien-1-ol, 10,11-epoxy-3,7,11-trimethyl-, (*E*,*E*)-] as a colorless oil (Note 10).

This material is acetylated with 35 ml. of pyridine and 35 ml. of acetic anhydride for 6 hours at room temperature. The mixture is then poured onto 250 g. of ice and extracted with five 75-ml. portions of ether. The combined ether extracts are washed successively with three 10-ml. portions each of saturated aqueous sodium bicarbonate and water and then dried over magnesium sulfate. It is important not to use strong acids such as hydrochloric or sulfuric acid to remove pyridine as was done in Part A, since they can destroy the acid-sensitive product.

Concentration of the ethereal solution at reduced pressure gives the epoxyacetate as a colorless oil more viscous than water. The overall yield based on farnesyl acetate is near 60% (Note 11). This material is reasonably pure if the preparation has been executed carefully, but it can be further purified by column chromatography (Note 12) or distillation (Note 13).

2. Notes

1. Farnesol was obtained from Fluka AG (Buchs, CH9470, Switzerland) as a mixture of 65% (*E*), (*E*)- and 35% (*Z*), (*E*)- isomers. It is also available from the Aldrich Chemical Company, Inc. This procedure works equally well with pure (*E*), (*E*)-farnesol, which may be obtained from the above mixture by careful distillation, at reduced pressure, through a Nester-Faust Teflon spinning-band column.

2. Pyridine was distilled from sodium hydroxide.

3. Infrared (neat) cm.$^{-1}$: 1740, 1240; proton magnetic resonance (CCl_4) δ, number of protons, multiplicity, coupling constant J in Hz.: 4.9–5.4 (3, multiplet, olefinic H), 4.46 (2, doublet, $J = 7$, CH_2O), 2.00 (3, singlet, O_2CCH_3).

4. Tetrahydrofuran or glyme work equally well in place of *tert*-butyl alcohol as a cosolvent, but they should be distilled under dry nitrogen

from lithium aluminum hydride[2] or sodium and benzophenone[3] prior to use. This procedure destroys peroxides which may be present.

5. The N-bromosuccinimide should be nearly white and uncontaminated by free bromine. If necessary, it may be recrystallized from hot water and stored in a refrigerator.

6. The submitters mixed active anhydrous silica gel with water (12% w/w) and stored it in a sealed container for at least 24 hours prior to use. A ratio of 60–80 g. of silica gel per gram of crude product was used for column chromatographic separations, and a column was chosen that would give a 10:1 height:diameter ratio of adsorbent. Columns were wet-packed with distilled petroleum ether (b.p. 60–68°), and after the crude product had been applied a step-gradient was run rapidly through 2% v/v ether in petroleum ether, 5% ether, and 10% ether. The column was then eluted with 20% v/v ether in petroleum ether until the bromohydrin acetate was obtained.

The checkers obtained roughly 30 g. of crude product in each run. Freshly opened Woelm silica gel (obtained from ICN Pharmaceuticals, 26201 Miles Ave., Cleveland, Ohio 44128) was deactivated as above, and 1800 g. was wet-packed with petroleum ether in a 65-mm. internal diameter column. In the first run the column was eluted as above, but a considerable amount of solvent was required to collect the product. Therefore, in the second run the crude product was applied to the column as a solution in petroleum ether, and 1-l. portions of 20% v/v ether:petroleum ether, 30% ether, 40% ether, 50% ether, 60% ether, and 70% ether were run through. None of these six fractions contained a significant weight of material. Elution with 2 l. of 80% v/v ether:petroleum ether then provided the bromohydrin acetate.

Fractions may be monitored by thin-layer chromatography on silica gel, developing with 10% v/v ethyl acetate in hexane and visualizing with iodine vapor. The following Rf values were observed: farnesol, 0.07; farnesyl acetate, 0.35; bromohydrin acetate, 0.20.

7. In each of two runs, the checkers obtained 25 g. (63% yield).

8. Infrared (neat) cm.$^{-1}$: 3520, 3450, 1740, 1235; proton magnetic resonance (CCl_4) δ, number of protons, multiplicity, coupling constant J in Hz.: 4.9–5.5 (2, multiplet, olefinic CH), 4.50 (2, doublet, $J = 7$, CH_2O), 3.7–4.0 (1, multiplet, $CHBr$), 2.00 (3, singlet, O_2CCH_3), 1.32 (6, singlet, O—$C(CH_3)_2$).

9. Using a smaller amount of K_2CO_3 made the reaction much slower and did not avoid or reduce the accompanying loss of the acetate group.

Pyridine at room temperature is not sufficiently basic to form the epoxide. Other bases were not tested.

10. Infrared (neat) cm.$^{-1}$: 3450, 2940, 1450, 1375; proton magnetic resonance (CCl_4) δ, number of protons, multiplicity, coupling constant J in Hz.: 5.0–5.5 (2, multiplet, olefinic CH), 3.97 (2, doublet, $J = 7$, OCH_2), 2.55 (1, triplet, $J = 6$, oxirane CH), 1.29 and 1.25 (6, two singlets, oxirane CH_3).

11. In each of two runs, the checkers obtained 19 g. (61% yield). Infrared (neat) cm.$^{-1}$: 2950, 1740, 1380, 1235; proton magnetic resonance (CCl_4) δ, number of protons, multiplicity, coupling constant J in Hz.: 5.0–5.5 (2, multiplet, olefinic CH), 4.48 (2, doublet, $J = 7$, OCH_2), 2.50 (1, triplet, $J = 6$, oxirane CH), 1.97 (3, singlet, O$_2$CCH_3), 1.23 and 1.21 (6, two singlets, oxirane CH_3).

12. Deactivation of silica gel and preparation of the column is carried out as in Note 6, except that the checkers consider 20 g. of silica gel per gram of crude product to be adequate in this case. Running through a gradient of petroleum ether containing increasing amounts of ether, the submitters found that the product was eluted with 15% v/v ether, and the checkers found that 25% v/v ether was required.

13. The submitters recommend distillation at 100° at less than 0.005 mm. The checkers distilled 1–2 g.-samples at 0.05 mm. (b.p. 113°) and at 0.15 mm. (b.p. 117°), and in both cases a clean product was obtained with high recovery.

3. Discussion

10,11-Epoxyfarnesol was first prepared by van Tamelen, Storni, Hessler, and Schwartz[4] using essentially this procedure. It is based on the findings of van Tamelen and Curphey[5] that N-bromosuccinimide in a polar solvent was a considerably more selective oxidant than others they tried. This method has been applied to produce terminally epoxidized mono-, sesqui-, di-, and triterpene systems for biosynthetic studies and bioorganic synthesis.[6] It has also been applied successfully in a simple synthesis of tritium-labeled squalene [2,6,10,14,18,22-Tetracosahexaene, 2,6,10,15,19,23-hexamethyl-, (all-E)-] and squalene-2,3-oxide [Oxirane, 2,2-dimethyl-3-(3,7,12,16,20-pentamethyl-3,7,11,-15,19-heneicosapentaenyl)-, (all-E)-],[7] and in the synthesis of Cecropia juvenile hormone.[8]

The oxidation procedure described above is intended to illustrate the selectivity that may be achieved using this system for functionalizing only one of several superficially similar double bonds in a molecule. In the case of acyclic terpenes, the yield of the desired terminal mono-bromohydrin decreases from 75–80% with geraniol ($C_{10}H_{18}O$) [2,6-Octadien-1-ol, 3,7-dimethyl-, (E)-] to 30–35% with squalene ($C_{30}H_{50}$). This is due to competing formation of polybromohydrins, allylic bromides, and bromocyclized material. The significant point, however, is that in all cases more than 95% of the monobromohydrin produced results from attack at the terminal double bond. A mechanistic investigation[9] showed that the N-bromosuccinimide was not merely providing a source of bromine or hypobromous acid, and that the reaction was promoted by acid and inhibited by base.

1. Department of Medicinal Chemistry, School of Pharmacy, University of Kansas, Lawrence, Kansas 66045.
2. L. F. Fieser and M. Fieser, "Reagents for Organic Synthesis," Vol. 1, John Wiley and Sons, Inc., New York, N.Y., 1967, p. 1140.
3. H. A. Staab and K. Wendel, *Org. Syn.*, Coll. Vol. 5, 201 (1973).
4. E. E. van Tamelen, A. Storni, E. J. Hessler, and M. Schwartz, *J. Amer. Chem. Soc.*, 85, 3295 (1963).
5. E. E. van Tamelen and T. J. Curphey, *Tetrahedron Lett.*, 121 (1962).
6. For leading references see E. E. van Tamelen and R. J. Anderson, *J. Amer. Chem. Soc.*, 94, 8225 (1972); E. E. van Tamelen, *Accounts Chem. Res.*, 1, 111 (1968).
7. R. Nadeau and R. Hanzlik, "Synthesis of Labeled Squalene and Squalene-2,3-Oxide," in *Methods in Enzymology*, Vol. 15, R. B. Clayton, ed., Academic Press, Inc., New York, N.Y., 1969, p. 346.
8. E. J. Corey, J. A. Katzenellenbogen, N. W. Gilman, S. A. Roman, and B. W. Erickson, *J. Amer. Chem. Soc.*, 90, 5618 (1968); E. E. van Tamelen and J. P. McCormick, *J. Amer. Chem. Soc.*, 92, 737 (1970).
9. E. E. van Tamelen and K. B. Sharpless, *Tetrahedron Lett.*, 2655 (1967).

2,3,4,5-TETRAHYDROPYRIDINE

[Pyridine, 2,3,4,5-tetrahydro-]

Submitted by GEORGE P. CLAXTON, LLOYD ALLEN,
and J. MARTIN GRISAR[1]
Checked by HENRY F. RUSSELL, RICHARD J. SUNDBERG,
and CARL R. JOHNSON

1. Procedure

A. *N-Chloropiperidine* [*Piperidine, 1-chloro-*]. A 500-ml., three-necked flask fitted with a mechanical stirrer, a dropping funnel, and a thermometer is charged with 170 g. (2.0 moles) of piperidine (Note 1). The flask is cooled in an acetone–ice bath, the piperidine is stirred, and 120 g. (2.0 moles) of glacial acetic acid is added dropwise at such a rate that the temperature does not exceed 10° (Note 2).

A 3-l., three-necked flask fitted with a mechanical stirrer, a dropping funnel, and a thermometer is then charged with an aqueous solution of 2.2 moles of calcium hypochlorite [Hypochlorous acid, calcium salt] (Note 3), and the piperidine acetate prepared above is placed in the dropping funnel. The hypochlorite solution is stirred and cooled to 0° to −5° with a methanol–ice bath, and the piperidine acetate is added dropwise over a period of 1.25 hours while the temperature is maintained below 0°. After a further 15 minutes of stirring, equal portions of the mixture are placed in two 2-l. separatory funnels and extracted three times with a total of about 1300 ml. of ether. The ether extract is placed in a 2-l. flask and dried over anhydrous sodium sulfate in a cold room at 4° overnight. After filtration to remove inorganic material, the bulk of the ether is removed by boiling on a water bath maintained below 60° (Note 4).

B. *2,3,4,5-Tetrahydropyridine Trimer*. In a 3-l., three-necked, round-bottomed flask equipped with a sealed mechanical stirrer, a dropping funnel, and a reflux condenser fitted with a calcium chloride drying tube are placed 264 g. (4.0 moles) of potassium hydroxide and 1250 ml. of absolute ethanol. This mixture is stirred with a Teflon paddle (Note 5) and heated to reflux to effect solution. The N-chloropiperidine solution prepared in Part A is then filtered through glass wool directly into the dropping funnel and added dropwise to the well-stirred, boiling reaction mixture over a period of ca. 2.5 hours (Note 6). The resulting mixture is stirred for a further 2 hours without heating and then allowed to stand at least 24 hours at room temperature, during which time tetrahydropyridine trimerizes. Precipitated potassium chloride is then removed by filtration, washed with two 150-ml. portions of absolute ethanol, and set aside for later use. The washes are combined with the filtrate, ethanol is distilled off on a steam bath under reduced pressure, and the distillate saved for further processing (Note 7). The residue remaining after distillation and the recovered potassium chloride are then combined in 750 ml. of water, and the resulting solution is extracted four times with a total of 500 ml. of ether. After standing over anhydrous magnesium sulfate for 4 hours, the extract is filtered and concentrated on a rotary evaporator with gentle warming. The resulting oily residue is dissolved in 75 ml. of acetone, and the solution is cooled to $-20°$ overnight. If no seed crystals are available, the walls of the flask are scratched with a glass rod to induce crystallization. The precipitate is collected by vacuum filtration and washed twice with 20-ml. portions of cold ($-20°$) acetone to give 64–80 g. (39–48%) of tetrahydropyridine trimer, m.p. 58–61° (Note 8).

2. Notes

1. Freshly distilled piperidine was used.

2. Ice was added to the mixture as required to dissolve any precipitated material and to keep the viscous solution clear.

3. MC and B Manufacturing Chemists HTH-grade 70% calcium hypochlorite was used. The solution required for the procedure was prepared by placing 680 g. of 70% calcium hypochlorite and 3 l. of water in a 5-l. flask and stirring overnight. The mixture was allowed to settle for several hours, and then the supernatant was vacuum-filtered through Celite and glass wool, giving enough hypochlorite solution for a single run. By centrifugation of the suspension remaining after decanting, enough hypochlorite solution for another run could be obtained. The molarity of the solution was determined by iodometric titration:

1 g. of potassium iodide was dissolved in 25 ml. of water, and 15 ml. of aqueous 10% sulfuric acid and 1 ml. of the hypochlorite solution were added. The red solution was titrated with aqueous 0.10N sodium thiosulfate [Thiosulfuric acid ($H_2S_2O_3$), disodium salt]. When the color changed to faint yellow, 1 ml. of starch solution was added, and the titration was continued to the colorless end point. The concentration was then determined according to the following formula:

$$\tfrac{1}{4}[(\text{ml. } Na_2S_2O_3 \text{ reagent})(\text{normality } Na_2S_2O_3)] = \text{molarity of } Ca(OCl)_2$$

4. *Caution! To avoid a rapid, spontaneous decomposition that results in complete loss of the chloropiperidine, the ether should not all be boiled off, nor should the temperature exceed 60°. The crude product should be used immediately in Part B.*

5. Use of a wire stirrer caused darkening of the ethanolic potassium hydroxide solution.

6. Isotripiperidein (m.p. 97–98°) is obtained if insufficient potassium hydroxide is used or if stirring is not sufficiently vigorous[2] (see Discussion).

7. Schöpf recommends that this solvent be reused in later runs.[2,3] The submitters found that substantial amounts of product can be recovered from this distillate after a few days of standing. Thus it appears that some tetrahydropyridine distils as monomer with the ethanol and trimerizes in the distillate. The checkers found that when the reaction was worked up after 24 hours of standing, the majority of the product was in the ethanol distillate. Therefore, they allowed the distillate to stand for several days, concentrated it by rotary evaporation, and crystallized the residue from acetone. The resulting tetrahydropyridine trimer was combined with that otherwise obtained.

8. Two trimers are known: α- (m.p. 60–62°) and β- (m.p. 70–73°) tripiperidein.[2] The β-form, usually obtained as a crude white solid melting at 40–68°, may be converted to the more stable α-isomer by recrystallizing from acetone containing 2% water.[2] α-Tripiperidein is best stored in a closed container over potassium hydroxide and may be kept for over a year in this manner.

3. Discussion

There is one standard procedure for preparing 2,3,4,5-tetrahydro-pyridine.[2,3] No acceptable alternative method is available, except that

N-chlorosuccinimide [2,5-Pyrrolidinedione, 1-chloro-] may be substituted for calcium hypochlorite in the first step.[4] Similar reaction sequences have been used to prepare substituted 2,3,4,5-tetrahydropyridines,[4,5] pyrroline [2H-Pyrrole, 3,4-dihydro-], and substituted pyrrolines.[7]

2,3,4,5-Tetrahydropyridine is useful for condensation with pyrroles and indoles,[6,8,9] β-ketoacids,[10-13] β-ketoesters,[14] and for a novel and very general reaction with magnesium chelates formed by reaction of methyl ketones with magnesium methyl carbonate [Magnesium, methoxy(methyl carbonato-O)-].[15,16] The highly reactive monomer trimerizes on standing to tripiperidein [1H,6H,11H-Tripyrido-[1,2-a:1′,2′-c:1″,2″-e][1,3,5]triazine, dodecahydro-], which occurs in two interconvertible crystalline forms designated as α and β:

In the absence of base, the trimer can rearrange to iso-tripiperidein, a product of self-condensation.[10,17] In the presence of base, however, α-tripiperidein is stable for over a year. In solution, tripiperidein readily detrimerizes to the monomer, which is in equilibrium with δ-aminovaleraldehyde [Pentanal, 5-amino-].[8]

1. Organic Chemistry Department, Merrell-National Laboratories, Division of Richardson-Merrell Inc., Cincinnati, Ohio 45215.
2. C. Schöpf, A. Komzak, F. Braun, and E. Jacobi, *Justus Liebigs Ann. Chem.*, **559**, 1 (1948).
3. C. Schöpf, H. Arm, and H. Krimm, *Chem. Ber.*, **84**, 690 (1951).
4. M. F. Grundon and B. E. Reynolds, *J. Chem. Soc. London*, 2445 (1964).
5. M. F. Grundon and B. E. Reynolds, *J. Chem. Soc. London*, 3898 (1963).
6. D. W. Fuhlhage and C. A. VanderWerf, *J. Amer. Chem. Soc.*, **80**, 6249 (1958).
7. R. Bonnet, V. M. Clark, A. Giddey, and A. Todd, *J. Chem. Soc. London*, 2087 (1959).
8. E. E. van Tamelen and G. G. Knapp, *J. Amer. Chem. Soc.*, **77**, 1860 (1955).
9. J. Thesing, S. Klüssendorf, P. Ballach, and H. Mayer, *Chem. Ber.*, **88**, 1295 (1955).
10. J. H. Wisse, H. de Klonia, and B. J. Visser, *Rec. Trav. Chim. Pays-Bas*, **85**, 865 (1966).
11. C. Schöpf, F. Braun, K. Burkhardt, G. Dummer, and H. Müller, *Justus Liebigs Ann. Chem.*, **626**, 123 (1959).
12. J. van Noordwijk, J. J. Mellink, B. J. Visser, and J. H. Wisse, *Rec. Trav. Chim. Pays-Bas*, **82**, 763 (1963).

13. J. H. Wisse, H. de Klonia, and B. J. Visser, *Rec. Trav. Chim. Pays-Bas*, **83**, 1265 (1964).
14. J. P. Rosazza, J. M. Bobbitt, and A. E. Schwarting, *J. Org. Chem.*, **35**, 2564 (1970).
15. G. P. Claxton, J. M. Grisar, E. M. Roberts, and R. W. Fleming, *J. Med. Chem.*, **15**, 500 (1972).
16. J. M. Grisar, G. P. Claxton, and K. T. Stewart, *Synthesis*, 284 (1974).
17. C. Schöpf, F. Braun, and A. Komzak, *Chem. Ber.*, **89**, 1821 (1956).

TRIFLUOROACETYLATION OF AMINES AND AMINO ACIDS UNDER NEUTRAL, MILD CONDITIONS: N-TRIFLUOROACETANILIDE AND N-TRIFLUOROACETYL-L-TYROSINE

[Acetamide, 2,2,2-trifluoro-*N*-phenyl- and L-Tyrosine, *N*-(trifluoroacetyl)-]

$$F_3CCCCl_3 + C_6H_5NH_2 \xrightarrow[25-35°]{(CH_3)_2SO} C_6H_5NHCCF_3 + CHCl_3$$

$$F_3CCCCl_3 + p\text{-HO}\!-\!C_6H_4CH_2CHCO_2H \xrightarrow[25-35°]{(CH_3)_2SO}$$
(NH_2)

$$p\text{-HO}\!-\!C_6H_4CH_2CHCO_2H + CHCl_3$$
(NHCCF_3, O)

Submitted by C. A. PANETTA[1]
Checked by R. M. FREIDINGER and G. BÜCHI

1. Procedure

A. *N-Trifluoroacetanilide.* In a two-necked, round-bottomed flask fitted with a thermometer, a Drierite tube, and a magnetic stirring bar are placed 4.56 ml. (4.66 g., 0.050 mole) of aniline [Benzenamine] (Note 1) and 15 ml. of dimethyl sulfoxide (Note 2). The resulting solution is stirred and cooled in an ice water bath, and when the internal temperature has dropped to 10–15°, 21.5 g. (0.10 mole) of 1,1,1-trichloro-3,3,3-trifluoroacetone [2-Propanone, 1,1,1-trichloro-3,3,3-trifluoro-] (Note 3) is added in portions through the condenser. A mild exotherm results, and the addition is extended over *ca.* 5 minutes to maintain the reaction mixture below 40°. When the addition is complete, the ice bath is removed, and the amber solution is stirred at room temperature for 22 hours. The reaction mixture is then poured into 750 ml. of water. A crystalline solid separates, and the resulting slurry is stirred for 1 hour before filtration. After being washed with water, the crystals are dried in a vacuum oven at 50° for 40 minutes to give 6.49–6.53 g. (69%) of *N*-trifluoroacetanilide, m.p. 86.0–86.5° (cor.) (Notes 4–6).

B. *N-Trifluoroacetyl-L-tyrosine.* In a two-necked, round-bottomed flask fitted with a thermometer, a condenser protected with a Drierite tube, and a magnetic stirrer are placed 18.12 g. (0.10 mole) of L-(-)-tyrosine (Note 7) and 130 ml. of dimethylsulfoxide (Note 2). The suspension is stirred and cooled in an ice water bath. When the internal temperature reaches 10–15°, 64.62 g. (0.30 mole) of 1,1,1-trichloro-3,3,3-trifluoroacetone (Note 3) is added through the condenser at a rate such that the temperature of the reaction mixture does not exceed 35°. The cooling bath is then removed, and the reaction mixture is stirred at room temperature for 22 hours, during which time the suspension becomes a solution. This solution is poured into 660 ml. of ice water, and the resulting mixture is extracted with two portions (660 ml. and 400 ml.) of 1-butanol. The organic extracts are concentrated, first on the rotary evaporator and then at 40° (0.1 mm.), to give a red–orange semisolid, which is dissolved in a minimum amount of acetone and placed on a column of silica gel (Note 8). Elution with benzene–acetone mixtures (Note 9) provides 20.0–22.2 g. (72–80%) of *N*-trifluoroacetyl-L-tyrosine as colorless to light yellow solid. Recrystallization from either benzene–acetone or water gives white needles, m.p. 192.5–193.5° (cor.) (Notes 6 and 10).

2. Notes

1. Commercial aniline from Fisher Scientific Company (purified-grade) was used as supplied.

2. Dimethyl sulfoxide from the J. T. Baker Chemical Company (reagent-grade) was used as supplied.

3. 1,1,1-Trichloro-3,3,3-trifluoroacetone is available from PCR, Inc., P.O. Box 14318, Gainesville, Florida. It may also be prepared easily by the following procedure. Fresh, anhydrous aluminum chloride (18.5 g., 0.139 mole) and 35.0 g. (0.192 mole) of chloropentafluoroacetone

[2-Propanone, 1-chloro-1,1,3,3,3-pentafluoro-] (b.p. 7.8°; available from PCR, Inc. or Allied Chemical Corp.) are combined in a flask fitted with a dry ice condenser and a magnetic stirring bar. The refluxing mixture is stirred for 4–6 hours and then allowed to warm gradually to room temperature. The contents of the flask are extracted three times with anhydrous ether, and the combined extracts are distilled at atmospheric pressure. After the ether has been removed, continued distillation gives 22.8–28.5 g. (55–69%) of 1,1,1-trichloro-3,3,3-trifluoroacetone, b.p. 83.5–84.5°, infrared (film) 1790 cm.$^{-1}$. This compound is stored at room temperature in a tightly stoppered bottle. In the absence of reliable toxicity data, it should be handled with normal precautions.

4. Infrared (CH_2Cl_2) cm.$^{-1}$: 3401 and 3049 (NH, CH), 1740 (C=O), 1235 (C—F). The literature m.p. for N-trifluoroacetanilide is 87.6°.[2]

5. The checkers suspected that some product was lost during the drying process. Therefore, they purified the crude product by sublimation at 55° (0.15 mm.), which gave 3.76–3.84 g. (80–81%) of N-trifluoroacetanilide in half-scale runs (Note 6).

6. The checkers ran Parts A and B at half the submitter's scale, and the yields were comparable or higher in all cases.

7. Reagent-grade L-(-)-tyrosine was obtained from Fisher Scientific Company.

8. Silica gel 60 (70–230 mesh) was purchased from E. Merck, Darmstadt, Germany.

9. The checkers, working at one half the submitter's scale, obtained 17.5 g. of crude product and used 175 g. of silica gel in their column. They eluted as follows:

Fraction	Eluent (Benzene:Acetone Ratio, ml.)	Eluate
1	9:1, 425	1.2 g., yellow oil
2	17:3, 100	1.7 g., pale yellow solid, m.p. 85–92°
3	3:1, 850	9.4 g., colorless solid, m.p. 194–196°
4	3:2, 600	0.4 g., colorless solid, m.p. 209–212°

Fraction 2 was recrystallized from benzene–acetone to give 1.2 g. of colorless solid, m.p. 194–196° (uncor.), which was combined with fraction 3 to give 10.6 g. (76%) of product.

10. Infrared (nujol) cm.$^{-1}$: 1695 (C=O), 1180 (C—F). The literature m.p. for N-trifluoroacetyl-L-tyrosine is 192.5–193.5°.[3]

3. Discussion

The original procedure for the trifluoroacetylation of amino acids used trifluoroacetic anhydride [Acetic acid, trifluoro-, anhydride].[4] This reagent, although inexpensive and readily available, has certain disadvantages: it is a highly reactive compound and thus has caused undesired reactions such as the cleavage of amide or peptide bonds,[5] unsymmetrical anhydrides are formed between the newly formed N-trifluoroacetylamino acids and the by-product trifluoroacetic acid, and excess trifluoroacetic anhydride has caused racemization of asymmetric centers.

Thus other trifluoroacetylation reagents have been investigated. S-Ethyl trifluorothioacetate [Ethanethioic acid, trifluoro-, S-ethyl ester][6] has none of the above disadvantages. It does require, however, weakly basic conditions (pH 8–9) and an aqueous medium. Phenyl

TABLE I

Trifluoroacetylamino Compounds Prepared with CF_3COCCl_3[a]

Product	Yield (%)
TFA-Aniline	69
TFA-L-Valine[L-Valine, N-(trifluoroacetyl)-]	94
TFA-DL-Phenylalanine[DL-Phenylalanine, N-(trifluoroacetyl)-]	52
TFA-L-Phenylalanine[L-Phenylalanine, N-(trifluoroacetyl)-]	57
TFA-L-Leucine[L-Leucine, N-(trifluoroacetyl)-]	100
TFA-L-Tyrosine	80
TFA-L-Proline[2-Pyrrolidinecarboxylic acid, 1-(trifluoroacetyl)-, (S)-]	100
TFA-DL-Alanine[DL-Alanine, N-(trifluoroacetyl)-]	20
TFA-Glycylglycine[Glycine, N-[N-(trifluoroacetyl)glycyl-]]	43
TFA-L-Prolylglycine, ethyl ester[Glycine, N-[1-(trifluoroacetyl)-L-prolyl]-, ethyl ester]	23
TFA-L-Asparagine[L-Asparagine, N^2-(trifluoroacetyl)-]	26
TFA-Dehydroabietylamine[Acetamide, 2,2,2-trifluoro-N-[[1,2,3,4,4a,9,10,10a-octahydro-1,4a-dimethyl-7-(1-methylethyl)-1-phenanthrenyl]methyl]-, [1R-(1α,4aβ,10aα)]-]	11

[a] Except for the first entry, all the compounds listed were prepared by the procedure of Part B.

trifluoroacetate [Acetic acid, trifluoro-, phenyl ester][7] effects trifluoro-acetylation of amino acids under essentially neutral conditions. Its main disadvantages are high cost and the elevated temperatures (120–150°) required.

1,1,1-Trichloro-3,3,3-trifluoroacetone is a relatively unreactive compound that is volatile and easily handled. It may be obtained either commercially or by a simple laboratory preparation (Note 3), and it trifluoroacetylates amino groups in amino acids and other compounds under neutral and extremely mild conditions.[8] Table I lists some compounds that have been prepared with this reagent.

1. Department of Chemistry, University of Mississippi, University, Mississippi 38677.
2. Beilstein, Second Supplement, Vol. XII, Springer-Verlag, Berlin, 1950, p. 141.
3. H. J. Shine and C. Niemann, *J. Amer. Chem. Soc.*, **74**, 97 (1952).
4. F. Weygand and E. Leising, *Chem. Ber.*, **87**, 248 (1954).
5. F. Weygand, R. Geiger, and U. Glocker, *Chem. Ber.*, **89**, 1543 (1956).
6. E. E. Schallenberg and M. Calvin, *J. Amer. Chem. Soc.*, **77**, 2779 (1955).
7. F. Weygand and A. Röpsch, *Chem. Ber.*, **92**, 2095 (1959).
8. C. A. Panetta and T. G. Casanova, *J. Org. Chem.*, **35**, 4275 (1970).

AMINOACETONE SEMICARBAZONE HYDROCHLORIDE[1]

CORRECTION

The product of step A formulated as acetamidoacetone is, in fact, the diacetyl derivative, N,N-diacetamidoacetone[2,3], as has been previously reported[4] under almost the same conditions as in the procedure. A sample of the product purified by a second distillation, b.p. 116–119° (1.5 mm.), followed by preparative t.l.c. (silica gel/ethyl acetate/Rf 0.45), had the following spectral properties[2]: mass spectrum m/e (relative intensity): 157 (M, 1), 115 (M—CH_2CO, 29), 72 (M—$2CH_2CO$—H, 39), 43 (CH_3CO, 100), 30 (CH_2=NH_2, 49), and a metastable peak at 84.2 corresponding to the 157 → 115 fragmentation; proton magnetic resonance (CCl_4) δ: 2.17 (3, CH_3COC), 2.28 (6, CH_3CON), 4.44 (2, CH_2); infrared (CCl_4) cm^{-1}: 1740, 1717, and 1703 (all C=O).

1. J. D. Hepworth, *Org. Syn.*, Coll. Vol. **5**, 27–29 (1973); **45**, 1–3 (1965).
2. P. J. Sidebottom, private communication, Sept. 25, 1975, The University, Southampton SO9 5NH, England. We are indebted to Mr. Sidebottom for providing the spectral data cited.
3. (a) S. I. Zav'yalov, private communication, Sept. 4, 1975, N. D. Zelinskii Institute of Organic Chemistry, Academy of Sciences, Moscow, U.S.S.R.; (b) H. F. v. Dobeneck, private communication, June 3, 1976, Technische Universität München, Munich, West Germany.
4. R. H. Wiley and O. H. Borum, *J. Amer. Chem. Soc.*, **70**, 2005–2006 (1948).

IODOMETHANE

WARNING

Iodomethane in high concentrations for short periods or in low concentrations for long periods can cause serious toxic effects in the central nervous system. Accordingly the American Conference of Governmental Industrial Hygienists[1] has set 5 p.p.m. as the highest average concentration in air to which workers should be exposed for long periods. This low level cannot be detected by smell. Therefore the preparation and use of iodomethane should always be performed in a well-ventilated fume hood. Since liquid iodomethane can be absorbed through the skin, care should be taken not to expose hands or other skin to liquid iodomethane.

1. American Conference of Governmental Industrial Hygienists (ACGIH), "Documentation of Threshold Limit Values," 3rd ed., Cincinnati, Ohio, 1971, p. 166.

OSHA LIST OF CARCINOGENS
WARNING

The following compounds are carcinogens and listed as such on the OSHA list. Rules to be followed when working with these substances were published in the Federal Register, Vol. **39**, No. 20, January 29, 1974.

2-Acetylaminofluorene
4-Aminobiphenyl
Benzidine
3,3'-Dichlorobenzidine
4'-Dimethylaminoazobenzene
alpha-Naphthylamine
beta-Naphthylamine
4-Nitrobiphenyl
N-Nitrosodimethylamine
beta-Propiolactone
bis-(Chloromethyl)ether
Chloromethyl methyl ether
4,4'-Methylene-*bis*(2-chloroaniline)
Ethyleneimine

AUTHOR INDEX

This Index comprises the names of contributors to Volume **56** only. For authors to previous volumes see Cumulative (Author) Index for Collective Volumes I-V and Author Indices of Annual Volumes **50-55.**

Allen, L., 118

Ban, Y., 49
Benkeser, R. A., 83
Brod, A. O., 59
Brossi, A., 3
Burgess, E. M., 40

Caine, D., 52
Chao, S. T., 52
Claxton, G. P., 118
Coxon, J. M., 25

Dansted, E., 25
Dolan, L. A., 3
Douglas, W. M., 1

Efraty, A., 1
Ehler, D. F., 83
Elphimoff-Felkin, I., 101

Garbisch, E. W., Jr., 107
Gariano, A. L., 59
Gariano, P., Jr., 59
Gassman, P. G., 15, 72
Grisar, J. M., 118
Gruetzmacher, G., 15
Guida, W. C., 59

Hanzlik, R. P., 112
Hartshorn, M. P., 25
Hino, T., 49
Hirai, K., 77

Ireland, R. E., 44

Jacobsen, N., 68

Kershaw, J. R., 19
King, R. B., 1
Kishida, Y., 77
Kiuchi, M., 49

Li, G. S., 83

McMurry, J. E., 36, 65
Melton, J., 36
Musser, J. H., 65

Nakagawa, M., 49
Neumeyer, J. L., 19

Obi, M., 49
Olofson, R. A., 88

Panetta, C. A., 122
Penton, H. R., Jr., 40

Raber, D. J., 59
Reeves, P. C., 28

Saegusa, J., 49
Sandler, S. R., 32
Sarda, P., 101
Shen, C. M., 95, 99
Smith, H. A., 52
Stadler, P. A., 8
Stütz, P., 8

Taylor, E. A., 40
Teitel, S., 3

SUBJECT INDEX

This Index comprises material from Volume 56 only. For subjects of previous volumes see Cumulative Indices of Collective Volumes I-V and Subject Indices of Annual Volumes 50-55.

This Index consists of two parts.

Part I contains entries referring to the names of compounds according to the Chemical Abstracts Systematic Nomenclature (see Index Guide, Chemical Abstracts vol. 76, 1972). The systematic name is followed by Chemical Abstracts Registry Number in brackets (see Chemical Abstracts Registry Handbook 1965-71 and Supplements) and page number.

Part II contains entries referring to the names of compounds as used by the authors of this Volume. Entries are followed by Chemical Abstracts Systematic name in brackets (if the name differs) and page number.

Entries in capital letters in **Part I** and **Part II** indicate compounds in the title of a preparation.

Part I

131

Unchecked Procedures

Received during the period July 1, 1975 – May 15, 1976

and

subsequently accepted for checking

In accordance with a policy adopted by the Board of Editors, beginning with Volume 50 and further modified in Volume 55 as noted in the Editor's Preface, procedures received by the Secretary during the year and subsequently accepted for checking by Organic Syntheses, will be made available for purchase at the price of $2 per procedure, prepaid, upon request to the Secretary:

> Dr. Wayland E. Noland, Secretary
> Organic Syntheses
> Department of Chemistry
> University of Minnesota
> Minneapolis, MN 55455

Payment must accompany the order, and should be made payable to Organic Syntheses, Inc. (not to the Secretary). Purchase orders not accompanied by payment will not be accepted. Procedures may be ordered by number and/or title from the list which follows.

It should be emphasized that the procedures which are being made available are unedited and have been reproduced just as they are first received from the submitters. There is no assurance that the procedures listed here will ultimately check in the form available, and some of them may be rejected for publication in Organic Syntheses during or after the checking process. For this reason, Organic Syntheses can provide no assurance whatsoever that the procedures will work as described, and offers no comment as to what safety hazards may be involved. Consequently, more than usual caution should be employed in following the directions in the procedures.

Organic Syntheses welcomes, on a strictly voluntary basis, comments from persons who attempt to carry out the procedures. For this purpose, a Checker's Report form will be mailed out with each unchecked procedure ordered. Procedures which have been checked by or under the supervision of a member of the Board of Editors will continue to be published in the volumes of Organic Syntheses, as in the past. It is anticipated that many of the procedures in the list will be published (often in revised form) in Organic Syntheses in future volumes.

                    – Wayland E. Noland

1973   Dibenzyl Sulfide

D. N. Harpp and R. A. Smith, Department of Chemistry, McGill
University, P. O. Box 6070, Station A, Montreal, Quebec, Canada
H3C 3G1

$$(C_6H_5CH_2)_2S_2 + [(CH_3)_2N]_3P \longrightarrow (C_6H_5CH_2)_2S + [(CH_3)_2N]_3PS$$

benzene
100^0 (97-99%)

1974   3-Trimethylsilyl-3-buten-2-one

R. K. Boeckman, Jr., D. M. Blum, B. Ganem, and N. Halvey,
Department of Chemistry, Wayne State University, Detroit, MI 48202

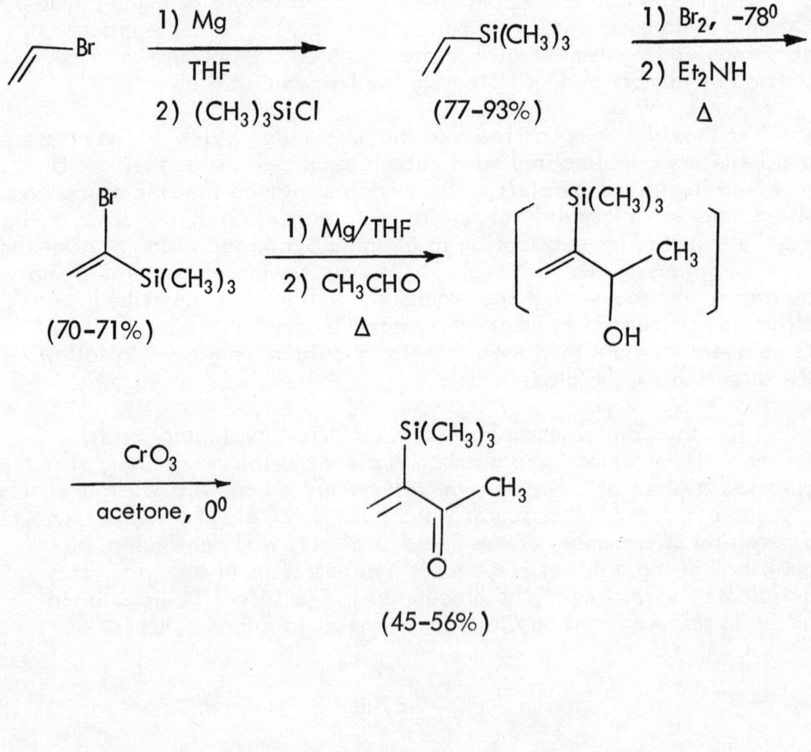

1975

cis-5,10-Dimethyl-$\Delta^{1,9}$-octal-2-one: Conjugate

Addition-Annelation of Unsaturated Ketones

R. K. Boeckman, Jr., D. M. Blum, and B. Ganem, Department of
Chemistry, Wayne State University, Detroit, MI 48202

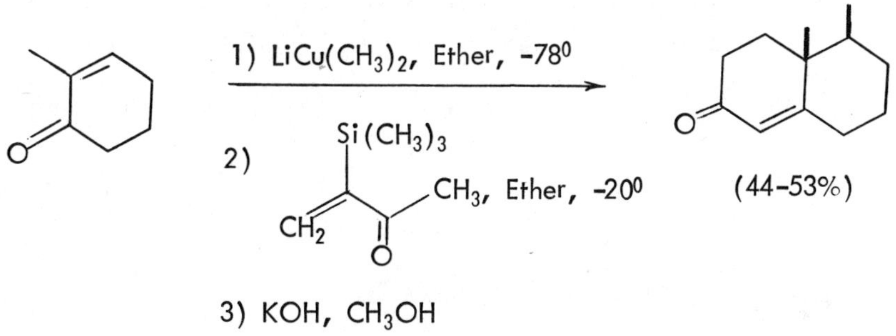

1) LiCu(CH$_3$)$_2$, Ether, −78^0

2) [Si(CH$_3$)$_3$ ... CH$_2$ ... CH$_3$], Ether, −20^0

3) KOH, CH$_3$OH

(44–53%)

1976

Dideuteriodiazomethane

S. M. Hecht, Department of Chemistry 18–407, Massachusetts Institute
of Technology, Cambridge, MA 02139

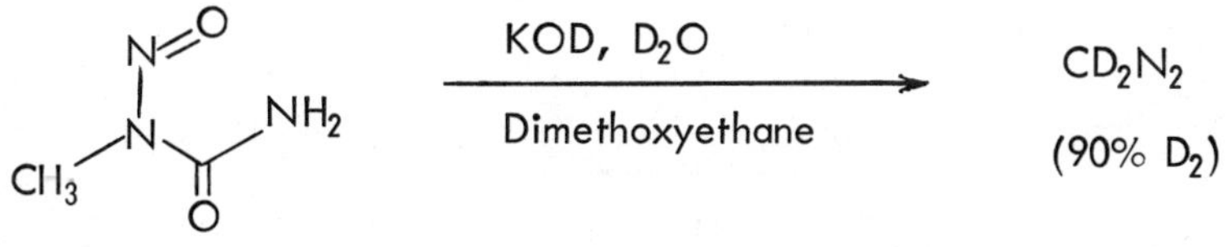

KOD, D$_2$O

Dimethoxyethane

CD$_2$N$_2$

(90% D$_2$)

Diethyl Phenylphosphate

J. F. Bunnett and R. H. Weiss, Department of Chemistry, Division of Natural Sciences-II, University of California, Santa Cruz, Santa Cruz, CA 90564

$$C_6H_5I + (C_2H_5O)_2PO^{\ominus} \ Na^{\oplus} \xrightarrow[NH_3]{h\nu} C_6H_5\overset{\displaystyle O}{\overset{\displaystyle \|}{P}}(OC_2H_5)_2 + NaI$$

(83%)

1983 Thiete 1,1-Dioxide

T. R. Nelson, J. E. Babiarz, J. T. Bartholomew, and D. C. Dittmer, Department of Chemistry, Syracuse University, Syracuse, N.Y. 13210

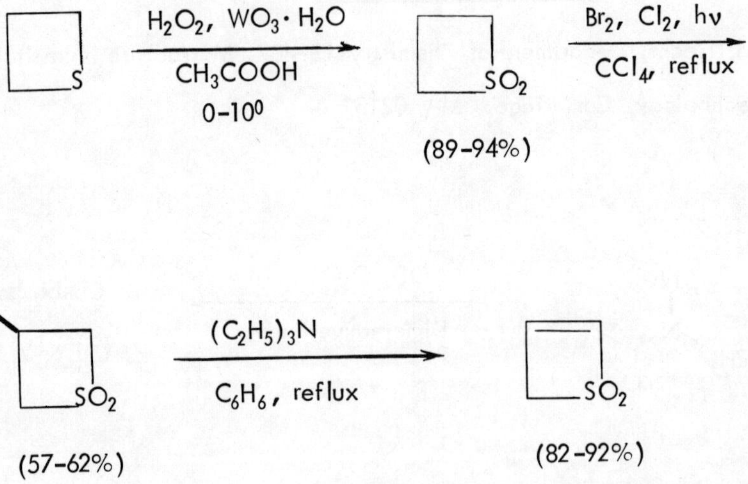

1984   <u>3-Phenylbutanenitrile</u>

J. A. Profitt and D. S. Watt, Department of Chemistry, University of

Colorado, Boulder, CO 80302

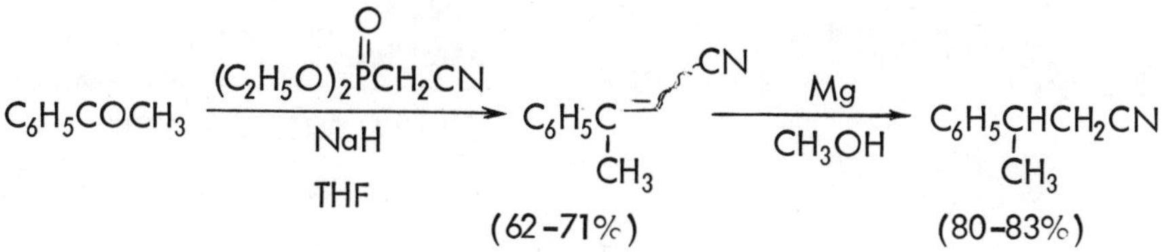

$$C_6H_5COCH_3 \xrightarrow[\substack{NaH \\ THF}]{(C_2H_5O)_2\overset{\overset{O}{\|}}{P}CH_2CN} \underset{(62-71\%)}{C_6H_5\underset{CH_3}{C}=\text{---}^{CN}} \xrightarrow[CH_3OH]{Mg} \underset{(80-83\%)}{C_6H_5\underset{CH_3}{CH}CH_2CN}$$

1985   <u>1H-Tetrazole Sodium Salt</u>

W. B. Blanchard and C. W. Ryan, Process Research and Development

Division, The Lilly Research Laboratories, Indianapolis, IN 46206

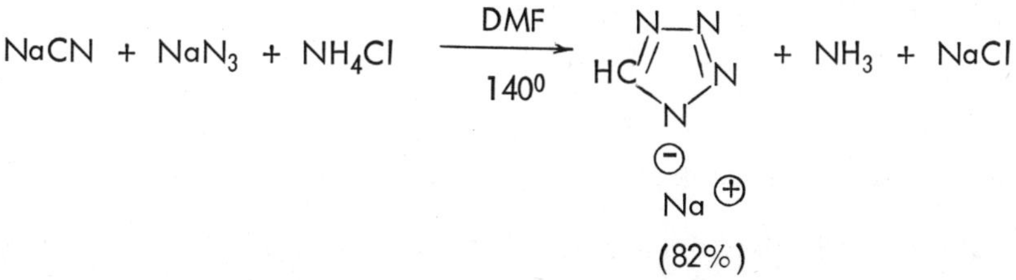

$$NaCN + NaN_3 + NH_4Cl \xrightarrow[140^0]{DMF} \underset{\substack{\ominus \\ Na^{\oplus} \\ (82\%)}}{\begin{matrix} N\text{---}N \\ HC \overset{/\!/}{\underset{N}{\diagdown}} \overset{\diagdown\!\diagdown}{N} \end{matrix}} + NH_3 + NaCl$$

1988   <u>Dimethyl 1,10-Decanedioate</u>

D. A. White, Monsanto Co., 800 N. Lindbergh Blvd., St. Louis,

MO 63166

$$2CH_3OOC(CH_2)_4COOH \xrightarrow[CH_3OH, CH_3ONa]{electricity} \underset{(75\%)}{CH_3OOC(CH_2)_8COOCH_3} + 2CO_2$$

D. A. White, Monsanto Co., 800 N. Lindbergh Blvd., St. Louis,
MO 63166

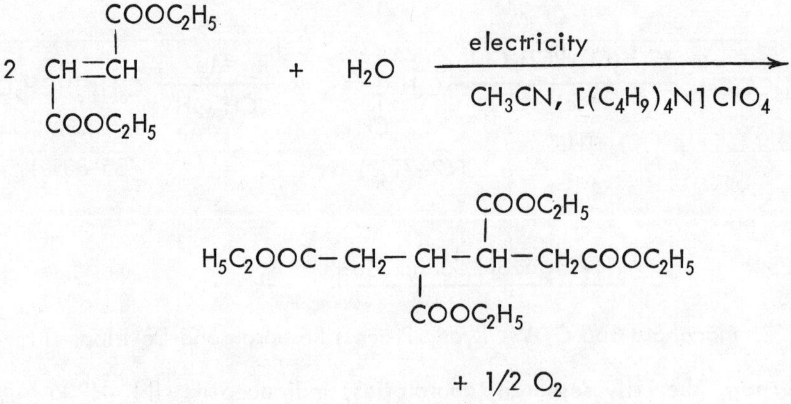

$$2 \quad \underset{\underset{COOC_2H_5}{|}}{\overset{\overset{COOC_2H_5}{|}}{CH=CH}} \quad + \quad H_2O \quad \xrightarrow[CH_3CN, \; [(C_4H_9)_4N]ClO_4]{electricity}$$

$$H_5C_2OOC-CH_2-\underset{\underset{COOC_2H_5}{|}}{\overset{\overset{COOC_2H_5}{|}}{CH-CH}}-CH_2COOC_2H_5$$

$$+ \; 1/2 \; O_2$$

(56%)

B. Haveau, M. Rens, A. R. Sidani, J. Toye, and L. Ghosez,
Laboratoire de Chimie Organique de Synthèse, Université de Louvain,
Place Louis Pasteur, 1, B-1348 Louvain-la-Neuve, Belgium

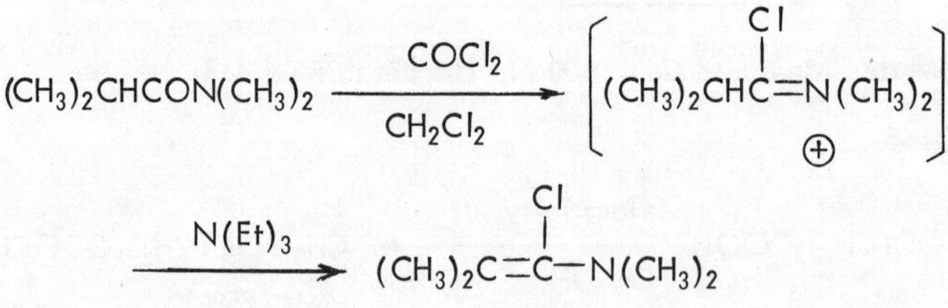

$$(CH_3)_2CHCON(CH_3)_2 \quad \xrightarrow[CH_2Cl_2]{COCl_2} \quad \left[(CH_3)_2CH\overset{\overset{Cl}{|}}{C}=\underset{\oplus}{N}(CH_3)_2 \right]$$

$$\xrightarrow{N(Et)_3} \quad (CH_3)_2C=\overset{\overset{Cl}{|}}{C}-N(CH_3)_2$$

(78-82%)

Deoxygenation of Epoxides with Lower Valent Tungsten
Halides: trans-Cyclododecene

M. A. Umbreit and K. B. Sharpless, Department of Chemistry,
Massachusetts Institute of Technology, Cambridge, MA 02139

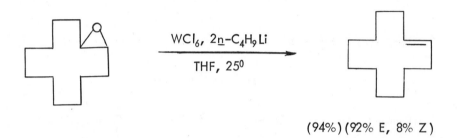

$$\xrightarrow[\text{THF, }25^0]{\text{WCl}_6,\ 2\underline{n}\text{-C}_4\text{H}_9\text{Li}}$$

(94%) (92% E, 8% Z)

Dialkyl and Alkyl Aryl Sulfides: Phenyl Neopentyl
Sulfide

D. Landini and F. Rolla, Centro C. N. R. e Istituto di Chimica
Industriale dell 'Universitá, Via C. Golgi 19, Milano 20133, Italy

$$(CH_3)_3CCH_2Br\ +\ C_6H_5SNa\ \xrightarrow[\text{H}_2\text{O}]{\overset{\oplus}{C_{16}H_{33}PBu_3}\ Br\ \overset{\ominus}{}}\ C_6H_5SCH_2C(CH_3)_3$$
$$+\ NaBr$$

(78–85%)

Substituted γ-Butyrolactones from Carboxylic Acids and Olefins: γ-(n-Octyl)-γ-butyrolactone

E. I. Heiba, R. M. Dessau, A. L. Williams, and P. G. Rodewald, Mobil Research and Development Corp., Central Research Division, P. O. Box 1025, Princeton, NJ 08540

$$4\,Mn(OAc)_2 \cdot 2\,H_2O + KMnO_4 + 8\,HOAc$$

$$\longrightarrow \quad 5\,Mn(OAc)_3 \cdot 2\,H_2O + KOAc + 2\,H_2O$$

$$Mn(OAc)_3 \cdot 2\,H_2O + Ac_2O \longrightarrow Mn(OAc)_3 \cdot H_2O + 2\,HOAc$$

$$2\,Mn(OAc)_3 \cdot H_2O + RCH{=}CH_2 \xrightarrow{\ NaOAc\ }$$

$$+\ 2\,Mn(OAc)_2 \cdot H_2O + HOAc$$

(66% based on $KMnO_4$ used)

1997 Nucleophilic α-sec-Aminoalkylation: 2-(Diphenylhydroxymethyl)pyrrolidine

D. Enders, R. Pieter, B. Renger, and D. Seebach, Institüt für Organische Chemie, der Justus Liebig-Universität, Fachbereich 14 Chemie, Heinrich-Buff-Ring 58, D-6300 Giessen, Germany

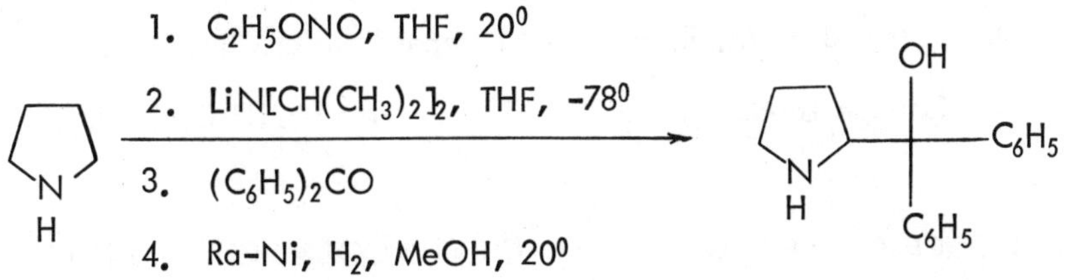
N
H
1. C2H5ONO, THF, 20°
2. LiN[CH(CH3)2]2, THF, -78°
3. (C6H5)2CO
4. Ra-Ni, H2, MeOH, 20°
OH
C6H5
N
H
C6H5

(60–65% based on benzophenone)

1998 Nitriles from Ketones: Cyclohexylnitrile

P. A. Wender, M. A. Eissenstat, N. Sapuppo, and F. E. Ziegler, Department of Chemistry, Harvard University, Cambridge, MA 02138

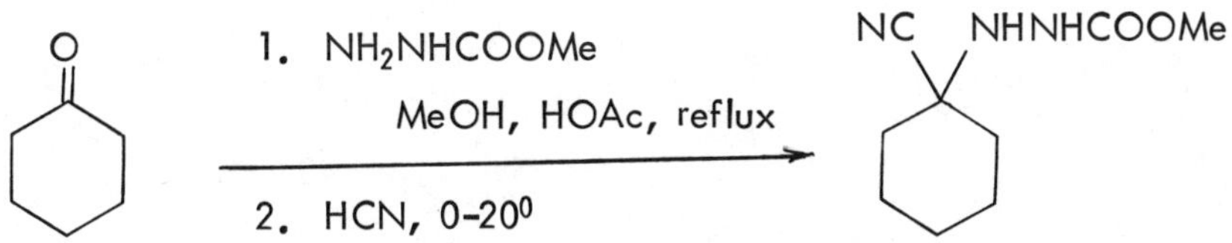
O
1. NH2NHCOOMe
MeOH, HOAc, reflux
2. HCN, 0-20°
NC NHNHCOOMe

(97%)

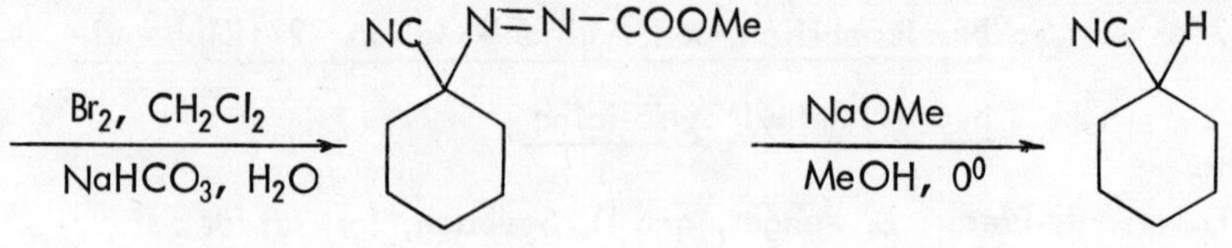

$$\xrightarrow[\text{NaHCO}_3,\ \text{H}_2\text{O}]{\text{Br}_2,\ \text{CH}_2\text{Cl}_2}$$

(93%)

$$\xrightarrow[\text{MeOH},\ 0^0]{\text{NaOMe}}$$

(92%)

2000   2α,4α-Dimethyl-8-oxabicyclo[3.2.1]oct-6-en-3-one

M. R. Ashcroft and H. M. R. Hoffmann, Department of Chemistry, University College London, 20 Gordon St., London WC1H OAJ, U. K.

$$\text{CH}_3\text{CH}_2\text{COCH}_2\text{CH}_3 + 2\,\text{Br}_2 \xrightarrow[0^0]{\text{PBr}_3} \text{CH}_3\text{CHBrCOCHBrCH}_3 + 2\,\text{HBr}$$

(65% of meso- and d,l-isomers)

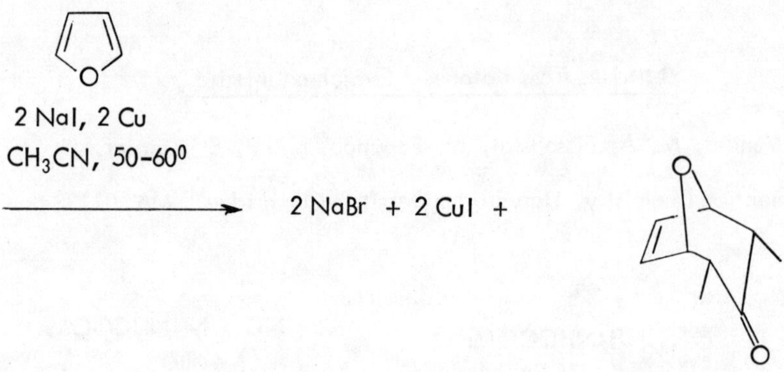

2 NaI, 2 Cu
CH$_3$CN, 50-60^0

$$\xrightarrow{\hspace{3cm}} 2\,\text{NaBr} + 2\,\text{CuI} +$$

(40-48%)

2003

Synthesis and Use of 1,2-Dicyanocyclobutene for in situ Generation of 2,3-Dicyanobutadiene as a Reactive Diene: 2,3-Dicyano-1,4,4a,9a-tetrahydrofluorene

D. Belluš, H. Sauter, and C. D. Weis, Central Research Laboratories, Ciba-Geigy AG., CH-4002 Basel, Switzerland

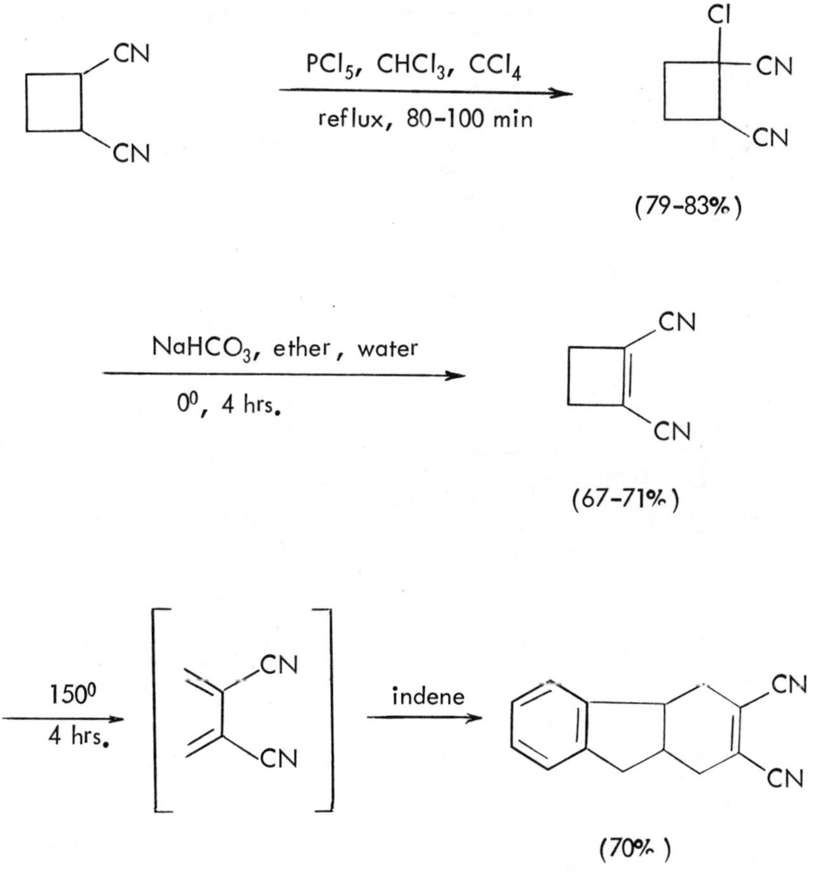

CN ... CN

$\xrightarrow{\text{PCl}_5,\ \text{CHCl}_3,\ \text{CCl}_4}$ reflux, 80–100 min

(79–83%)

$\xrightarrow[0^0,\ 4\ \text{hrs.}]{\text{NaHCO}_3,\ \text{ether, water}}$

(67–71%)

$\xrightarrow[4\ \text{hrs.}]{150^0}$

indene

(70%)

C. M. Dougherty and R. A. Olofson, Department of Chemistry,

Herbert H. Lehman College of the City of New York, Bedford Park

Blvd. W., Bronx, NY 10468

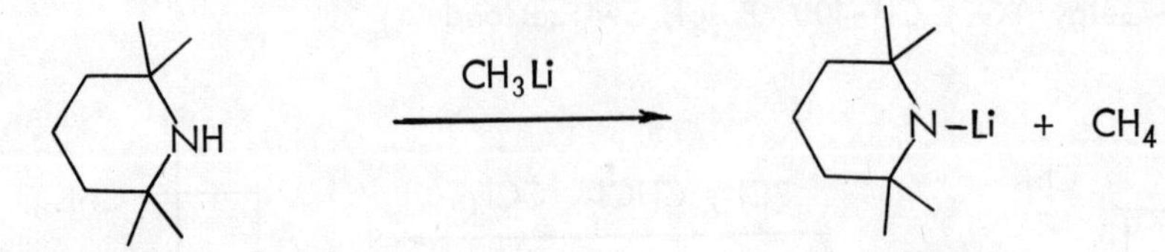

[HTMP]

[Li TMP]

("100%")

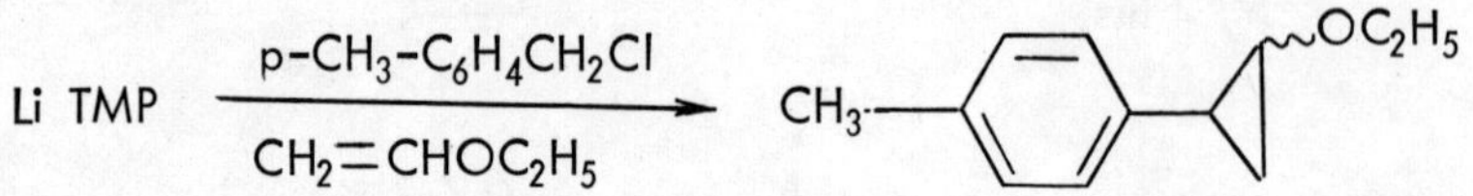

Li TMP

(76%)

+ HTMP + LiCl

Preparation and Reaction of Highly Reactive Magnesium

Metal

R. D. Rieke, S. E. Bales, and P. M. Hudnall, Department of Chemistry, University of North Carolina, Chapel Hill, NC 27514

$$MgCl_2 + K + KI \xrightarrow{\text{THF, } 66^0} Mg + \text{alkali salts}$$

$$\xrightarrow[-78^0]{C_6H_5Br} C_6H_5MgBr \xrightarrow[\text{2) 20\% HCl}]{\text{1) } CO_2} C_6H_5COOH$$

$$(70\text{-}89\%)$$

Preparation of Ketones from Organoboranes by the

Cyanoborate Process: Di-n-octyl Ketone

A. Pelter, A. Jones, and K. Smith, Department of Chemistry, University of Wales, University College of Swansea, Singleton Park, Swansea SA2 8PP, U.K.